METHUEN'S MONOGRAPHS ON PHYSICAL SUBJECTS

General Editor: B. L. WORSNOP, B.SC., PH.D.

WAVE GUIDES

Wave Guides

H. R. L. LAMONT

M.A., PH.D.

Research Physicist, Research Laboratories of the
General Electric Co. Ltd., Wembley, England

WITH 37 DIAGRAMS

LONDON: METHUEN & CO. LTD.
NEW YORK: JOHN WILEY & SONS, INC.

First published June 1942
Second Edition May 1946
Third Edition, Revised, May 1950
Reprinted 1953 and 1959

3.3
CATALOGUE NO. 4034/U (METHUEN)

PRINTED AND BOUND IN GREAT BRITAIN BY
BUTLER AND TANNER LTD, FROME AND LONDON

PREFACE

In a volume of this size it is not possible to deal fully with the various branches of wave guide development. Accordingly, it was considered of most value to the student and the research worker to present the essential parts of the theory, giving the more useful expressions in some detail. The experimental side has received rather scant mention, but the classified bibliography will assist the reader who wishes to acquire the experimental technique. He is assured that the subject provides plenty of scope for his ingenuity.

My thanks are due to the editors of the *Bell System Technical Journal* and the *Journal of Applied Physics* for permission to include Figures 7 and 10 respectively, and I gratefully acknowledge the assistance received from my colleague, Dr. J. E. Houldin.

H. R. L. L.

WEMBLEY
  MIDDLESEX
April 1942

PREFACE TO THE THIRD EDITION

SINCE this book was first published the ramifications of the subject have greatly expanded, and what was an experimental science has become a highly organized branch of radio engineering. In this edition a new chapter gives the principles of some of the more fundamental developments, although unfortunately the complexities of the theory often place a detailed analysis beyond our scope. The basic theory remains unchanged, but a number of new sections have been added throughout the text, modifications have been made to indicate modern trends, and the bibliography has been brought up to date.

H. R. L. L.

WEMBLEY

January 1949

CONTENTS

CHAPTER I

INTRODUCTION TO WAVE GUIDE THEORY

HISTORICAL SKETCH

ELECTROMAGNETIC waves may be regarded, from a communications point of view, as divisible into two main types, *free waves* and *guided waves*. The radiation from a dipole situated in free space is an example of the first type; waves on a parallel wire line are of the second type. The energy of free waves spreads out more or less in all directions in space, but in a guided wave it is confined to the vicinity of the guiding system. Thus, by suitable choice of the guiding system, energy may be transferred from place to place with little loss.

In radio engineering the normal method of guiding energy is by means of transmission lines consisting of two or more conductors, the most usual being a line of two parallel wires or of two coaxial tubes. These types have long been familiar and their properties are well known. The fact that electromagnetic energy may be guided in the interior of a single hollow conductor is less familiar, although this was proved towards the end of the last century. To allow free transmission of the energy, however, very high frequencies have to be employed, and on account of the difficulty of generating such frequencies the work was regarded as of academic interest only. Progress in the design of short-wave oscillators has made available for radio transmission a steadily increasing range of frequencies, and in 1936 attention was drawn to the possibilities of this almost forgotten type of transmission line in papers coming almost simultaneously from two

American sources [18], [19], [20], one of which introduced the name *Wave Guide* for the hollow conductor. These were followed by many contributions, from America, France, and Germany in particular, which contain much theoretical and experimental work.

It is mainly the elements of the theory of wave guides which will be discussed here, and they will be considered separately under three main divisions : hollow conductors as transmission lines, as resonators, and as radiators. The more modern developments will be referred to in the text, but it will be appropriate to give here a sketch of the historical development of the subject up to 1936.

In his *Recent Researches* published in 1894, J. J. Thomson dealt shortly with oscillations inside a cylinder, and in the same year Sir Oliver Lodge [1] demonstrated to members of the Royal Institution the radiation of waves from—to quote his own words—' the inside of a hollow cylinder with sparks at the ends of a diameter ; this being a feeble radiator, but a very persistent resonator '. The problem was investigated more fully in 1897 by Lord Rayleigh [2], who showed theoretically that, in perfectly conducting rectangular and circular cylinders, two classes of wave are possible. For each class there is a series of characteristic wave forms, with a limiting frequency for each type below which no propagation occurs. The allied problem of the transmission of waves along a single dielectric cylinder was studied theoretically in Germany by Hondros and Debye [28], who produced a paper on the subject in 1910, showing that at suitably high frequencies such propagation was possible. Initial experiments intended to verify this theory were described by Zahn [29] in 1916, and the verification for waves propagated in glass cylinders was later given by Schriever [30]. The papers published in 1936 by Barrow [18], and by Southworth and his collaborators at the Bell Telephone Laboratories [19], [20], dealt for the first time with the attenuation which guided waves would suffer from imperfect conductors and dielectrics, and showed that this was sufficiently low to make such wave guides more efficient transmission lines at very high frequencies than the familiar parallel wire and coaxial lines.

During the early days of electromagnetics the theory of oscillations inside closed hollow conductors was developed, and the particular cases of cylinders, spheres, ellipsoids, &c., were discussed by a number of authors. References to this work will be found in Bateman's *Electrical and Optical Wave Motion*.†

On the problem of radiation from open-ended wave guides there appears to have been no particular investigation before 1934, when Bergmann and Krügel [52] made some measurements on the radiation field of a dipole placed inside a hollow cylinder. However, it was only after 1900 that the difficulties of a theory of diffraction consistent with Maxwell's equations were being appreciated and resolved, and this work made possible the recent studies of the radiation patterns produced by wave guides.

FUNDAMENTAL ELECTROMAGNETIC THEORY

In dealing with transmission inside a hollow conductor we have to abandon the usual concepts of current and voltage, for here, in the absence of a second conductor, there is no ordinary ' flow and return ' circuit, and it is logical to use the more fundamental conception of a field of force characterized by electric and magnetic vectors. Maxwell's field equations for the electric force E and the magnetic force H in a homogeneous isotropic dielectric of permeability μ and dielectric constant ε are

$$\left.\begin{aligned} \frac{\varepsilon}{c}\frac{\partial E}{\partial t} &= \operatorname{curl} H \\ -\frac{\mu}{c}\frac{\partial H}{\partial t} &= \operatorname{curl} E. \end{aligned}\right\} \qquad . \quad . \quad . \quad (\text{1.1})$$

† Cambridge, 1915.

They imply also that E and H have zero divergence, i.e.

$$\text{div } E = 0, \quad \text{div } H = 0. \qquad . \qquad . \quad (1.2)$$

We shall use the Gaussian system of units, in which all electrical quantities are in c.g.s. electrostatic units, and all magnetic quantities are in c.g.s. electromagnetic units. In these the dielectric constant and permeability of free space are each unity. The velocity of light in the medium, $c/(\varepsilon\mu)^{\frac{1}{2}}$, will be represented by v.

The metallic conductor which forms the bounding surface of the dielectric space will provide boundary conditions to be satisfied by the solutions of (1.1). For a perfect conductor the condition is that components of electric field in the dielectric which are tangential to the boundary surface are zero at that surface.

As any vibration can be resolved into a sum of simple harmonic vibrations it will be sufficient to study the case when the field vectors vary with time according to the factor $\exp(i\omega t)$, where $\omega = 2\pi f$, f being the frequency. As is common practice, this factor will usually be omitted from expressions for oscillating fields, but its presence is always implicit.

RECTANGULAR WAVE GUIDES

A wave guide of rectangular cross-section and of infinite length is mathematically the most simple, and will be treated first. The conductivity of the metal conductor is assumed infinite, and the interior filled with a loss-free dielectric.

Let Figure 1 represent a section of a rectangular wave guide with sides of lengths a and b related as shown to a system of rectangular axes, in which the z axis is parallel to the axis of the tube. For a wave propagated in the positive direction of z it can be assumed that the dependence on the z-coordinate is of the form $\exp(-\gamma z)$, where γ is

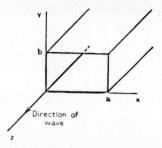

y

b

Direction of
wave

z

a

x

FIG. 1.—Coordinate system for rectangular guide.

the propagation constant. Equations (1.1) then become,
in their component form,

$$
\left.
\begin{aligned}
\frac{i\omega\varepsilon}{c} E_x &= \frac{\partial H_z}{\partial y} + \gamma H_y \\
\frac{i\omega\varepsilon}{c} E_y &= -\gamma H_x - \frac{\partial H_z}{\partial x} \\
\frac{i\omega\varepsilon}{c} E_z &= \frac{\partial H_y}{\partial x} - \frac{\partial H_x}{\partial y},
\end{aligned}
\right\} \quad \cdots \quad (1.3)
$$

$$
\left.
\begin{aligned}
\frac{i\omega\mu}{c} H_x &= -\frac{\partial E_z}{\partial y} - \gamma E_y \\
\frac{i\omega\mu}{c} H_y &= \gamma E_x + \frac{\partial E_z}{\partial x} \\
\frac{i\omega\mu}{c} H_z &= -\frac{\partial E_y}{\partial x} + \frac{\partial E_x}{\partial y}.
\end{aligned}
\right\} \quad \cdots \quad (1.4)
$$

Using the first two equations of each set we deduce

$$
\left.
\begin{aligned}
k^2 E_x &= -\frac{i\omega\mu}{c} \frac{\partial H_z}{\partial y} - \gamma \frac{\partial E_z}{\partial x} \\
k^2 E_y &= \frac{i\omega\mu}{c} \frac{\partial H_z}{\partial x} - \gamma \frac{\partial E_z}{\partial y} \\
k^2 H_x &= \frac{i\omega\varepsilon}{c} \frac{\partial E_z}{\partial y} - \gamma \frac{\partial H_z}{\partial x} \\
k^2 H_y &= -\frac{i\omega\varepsilon}{c} \frac{\partial E_z}{\partial x} - \gamma \frac{\partial H_z}{\partial y},
\end{aligned}
\right\} \quad \cdots \quad (1.5)
$$

where k is defined by the equation

$$k^2 = \frac{\omega^2}{v^2} + \gamma^2. \quad . \quad . \quad . \quad (1.6)$$

Substitution of these values of E_x, E_y, H_x, H_y in the third equations of (1.3) and (1.4) gives

$$\frac{\partial^2 E_z}{\partial x^2} + \frac{\partial^2 E_z}{\partial y^2} + k^2 E_z = 0$$

$$\frac{\partial^2 H_z}{\partial x^2} + \frac{\partial^2 H_z}{\partial y^2} + k^2 H_z = 0.$$

These are two linearly independent equations in E_z and H_z of the form

$$\frac{\partial^2 \phi}{\partial x^2} + \frac{\partial^2 \phi}{\partial y^2} + k^2 \phi = 0, \quad . \quad . \quad . \quad (1.7)$$

and so the investigation can be split up into sections,

   (1) $H_z \equiv 0$, E_z a solution of (1.7)
   (2) $E_z \equiv 0$, H_z a solution of (1.7)

and a trivial case where

   (3) $E_z = H_z \equiv 0$.

The last set of conditions makes all the components zero, i.e. the wave disappears, unless $k^2 = 0$. It will be shown in Chapter II that k^2 can be zero only when there is another conductor inside the tube. Cases (1) and (2) define the two basic types of wave which can be propagated. The first, which has its magnetic vector in a plane normal to the direction of propagation, but has a component of electric force in the direction of propagation, is called a *transverse magnetic* or *E wave*. The second, having entirely transverse electric force and an axial component of magnetic force, is called a *transverse electric* or *H wave*. The wave representing the general solution of the equations will be a linear combination of these two types.

   The solution of (1.7) is seen to be

$$\phi = \frac{\sin}{\cos} k_1 x \frac{\sin}{\cos} k_2 y, \quad . \quad . \quad . \quad (1.8)$$

where $k_1{}^2 + k_2{}^2 = k^2$. This can now be applied to determine the E and H wave types.

E Waves. The expression for E_z will be

$$E_z = \sin k_1 x \sin k_2 y \, e^{-\gamma z}. \qquad . \qquad (1.9)$$

The cosine solution is omitted since E_z, being tangential to the boundary walls $x = 0$ and $y = 0$, must be zero for these values. The boundary walls $x = a$ and $y = b$ also impose the conditions

$$\sin k_1 a = 0, \qquad \sin k_2 b = 0,$$

i.e. $\qquad k_1 a = m\pi, \qquad k_2 b = n\pi,$

where m and n are positive integers. Hence

$$k^2 = \left(\frac{m\pi}{a}\right)^2 + \left(\frac{n\pi}{b}\right)^2. \qquad . \qquad . \qquad (1.10)$$

The propagation constant γ is now determined from equation (1.6);

$$\gamma^2 = \left(\frac{m\pi}{a}\right)^2 + \left(\frac{n\pi}{b}\right)^2 - \left(\frac{\omega}{v}\right)^2. \qquad . \qquad . \qquad (1.11)$$

This defines an infinite number of modes dependent on the integral values given to m and n. Of these only a finite number will be transmission modes, since for free transmission γ must be a pure imaginary, and so the frequency must be so high that

$$\frac{\omega}{v} > \left[\left(\frac{m\pi}{a}\right)^2 + \left(\frac{n\pi}{b}\right)^2\right]^{\frac{1}{2}}. \qquad . \qquad . \qquad (1.12)$$

Putting $\gamma = \alpha + i\beta$, where α represents the attenuation constant and β the phase constant, we obtain, under condition (1.12),

$$\alpha = 0, \quad \beta = \left[\left(\frac{\omega}{v}\right)^2 - \left(\frac{m\pi}{a}\right)^2 - \left(\frac{n\pi}{b}\right)^2\right]^{\frac{1}{2}}, \quad . \qquad (1.13)$$

or, putting it in terms of the wavelength λ in the unbounded dielectric and the wavelength λ_t measured inside the tube,

$$\frac{1}{\lambda_t} = \frac{\beta}{2\pi} = \left[\frac{1}{\lambda^2} - \left(\frac{m}{2a}\right)^2 - \left(\frac{n}{2b}\right)^2\right]^{\frac{1}{2}}. \qquad . \qquad (1.14)$$

With an equality sign, equation (1.12) determines the *critical* or *cut-off frequency* f_0, which forms the boundary between the transmission and attenuation regions. Above this frequency the attenuation is zero; below it α assumes a finite value and the wave suffers rapid exponential attenuation. The *critical wavelength*, corresponding to the critical frequency, is given by

$$\lambda_0 = 2 \Big/ \left[\left(\frac{m}{a} \right)^2 + \left(\frac{n}{b} \right)^2 \right]^{\frac{1}{2}}, \quad . \quad . \quad (1.15)$$

with the understanding that λ_0 is the wavelength in the *unbounded* dielectric of an oscillation of frequency f_0. At this frequency the wavelength measured in the tube is infinite.

The other components of E and H can be calculated from equation (1.5), the complete set being

$$\left.\begin{aligned}
E_z &= \sin \frac{m\pi x}{a} \sin \frac{n\pi y}{b} e^{-i\beta z} \\[4pt]
E_x &= -\frac{i\beta}{k^2} \frac{m\pi}{a} \cos \frac{m\pi x}{a} \sin \frac{n\pi y}{b} e^{-i\beta z} \\[4pt]
E_y &= -\frac{i\beta}{k^2} \frac{n\pi}{b} \sin \frac{m\pi x}{a} \cos \frac{n\pi y}{b} e^{-i\beta z} \\[4pt]
H_z &= 0 \\[4pt]
H_x &= \frac{i\omega\varepsilon}{k^2 c} \frac{n\pi}{b} \sin \frac{m\pi x}{a} \cos \frac{n\pi y}{b} e^{-i\beta z} \\[4pt]
H_y &= -\frac{i\omega\varepsilon}{k^2 c} \frac{m\pi}{a} \cos \frac{m\pi x}{a} \sin \frac{n\pi y}{b} e^{-i\beta z}
\end{aligned}\right\} . \quad (1.16)$$

H Waves. In this case the longitudinal magnetic component will be given by

$$H_z = \cos k_1 x \cos k_2 y \, e^{-\gamma z}, \quad . \quad . \quad (1.17)$$

since this form satisfies the conditions that E_x and E_y, which by (1.5) are proportional to $\partial H_z/\partial y$ and $\partial H_z/\partial x$ respectively, should vanish at the boundaries $y = 0$ and $x = 0$, to which they are tangential. The other two boundaries require $k_1a = m\pi$, $k_2b = n\pi$ as before, so that the relations (1.10)–(1.15) hold also for H waves.

The expressions for the components of E and H are (omitting, as throughout, an arbitrary amplitude constant)

$$
\left.
\begin{aligned}
H_z &= \cos \frac{m\pi x}{a} \cos \frac{n\pi y}{b} e^{-i\beta z} \\
H_x &= \frac{i\beta}{k^2} \frac{m\pi}{a} \sin \frac{m\pi x}{a} \cos \frac{n\pi y}{b} e^{-i\beta z} \\
H_y &= \frac{i\beta}{k^2} \frac{n\pi}{b} \cos \frac{m\pi x}{a} \sin \frac{n\pi y}{b} e^{-i\beta z} \\
E_z &= 0 \\
E_x &= \frac{i\omega\mu}{k^2 c} \frac{n\pi}{b} \cos \frac{m\pi x}{a} \sin \frac{n\pi y}{b} e^{-i\beta z} \\
E_y &= -\frac{i\omega\mu}{k^2 c} \frac{m\pi}{a} \sin \frac{m\pi x}{a} \cos \frac{n\pi y}{b} e^{-i\beta z}
\end{aligned}
\right\} \quad (1.18)
$$

PROPERTIES OF THE WAVE TYPES

We have shown that various forms of E and H wave are possible, with characteristics dependent on the values given to the parameters m and n. They can have integral values only, and these are limited for given dimensions and a given impressed frequency by the inequality (1.12).

It is convenient to denote the wave type by suffixes, as E_{mn} or H_{mn}. The critical frequency is lowest for the lowest permissible values of m and n, and it increases as m or n is increased. Types E_{00}, E_{01} and E_{10} do not exist, since for these all the components given by (1.16) vanish, and thus the E wave of the lowest order physically realizable is the E_{11} type. All higher-order types such as E_{12} and E_{21} are theoretically possible. The lowest-order H wave is H_{01} or H_{10}, all components of the H_{00} type being identically zero.[†]

[†] An alternative notation is TM (transverse magnetic) and TE (transverse electric) for E and H modes respectively. The E,H notation is given preference in B.S. 204, Supplement No. 1 (1948), ' Glossary of terms used in waveguide practice '.

The form at any instant of the lines of force of the various wave types may be obtained from the differential equation of the lines of force, which, for the electric lines, is

$$\frac{dx}{E_x} = \frac{dy}{E_y} = \frac{dz}{E_z}. \qquad \cdots \qquad (1.19)$$

For the simple case of an E_{11} wave in a tube of square section this becomes

$$\tan \frac{\pi x}{a} \, dx = \tan \frac{\pi y}{a} \, dy = -\frac{a\beta}{2\pi} \tan \beta z \, dz,$$

of which the solutions are readily found to be

$$\cos \frac{\pi x}{a} = C_1 \cos \frac{\pi y}{a}$$

$$\cos^2 \frac{\pi x}{a} \cos \beta z = C_2.$$

The lines of force given by these equations are drawn in Figure 2, which also shows the patterns of several other

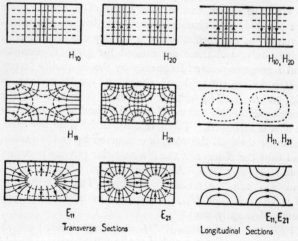

FIG. 2.—Lines of force of waves in a rectangular guide.
Full lines, electric force ; dashed lines, magnetic force.

types of wave. The values of the subscripts m, n determine the number of half-sinusoids in the distribution of field intensity along the sides a and b respectively. The type H_{10} is of special interest, since it has the simplest configuration of all hollow tube waves. The electric field has only one component, which is parallel to the side of length b, and has a half-sinusoidal amplitude distribution along the side a. The propagation constant and critical frequency are dependent only upon the dimension a, the critical wavelength being given by the simple expression $\lambda_0 = 2a$. Critical wavelengths for a few wave types in an air-filled tube of square section are:

Wave	λ_0	Wave	λ_0
H_{10}	$2 \cdot 000a$	H_{20}	$1 \cdot 000a$
E_{11}, H_{11}	$1 \cdot 414a$	E_{12}, H_{12}	$0 \cdot 894a$

As an example, for a 5-cm. square tube the two longest critical wavelengths are 10 cm. and 7·1 cm. These limits would be increased if the tube were filled with an insulator of higher dielectric constant. The losses at high frequency of known solid or liquid dielectrics are, however, so high as to make their use impracticable. If tubes of economical dimensions are to be used, wavelengths must be of the order of ten centimetres and below.

Under suitable conditions it will be possible to propagate simultaneously in the tube a number of types of wave, each of which will have its own wave pattern and, as is shown later, its own speed of propagation. The relative amplitudes of these different forms are governed by the terminal conditions of the tube, i.e. by the geometry of the generating and receiving devices, and by the current distributions in them. By suitable design of these, a particular wave can be emphasized to the practical exclusion of the others. Terminal devices for transmitting and receiving are constructed according to the principle that conductors, one or more, are placed inside the tube so as

to coincide with lines of electric force of the field patterns
of the desired wave. These are fed with current of
suitable frequency, consideration being given to the correct
phasing if more than one conductor is used. A few
examples are shown in Figure 3. The problem of the

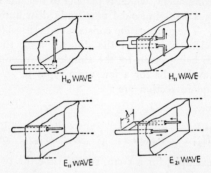

H_{10} WAVE

H_{11} WAVE

E_{11} WAVE

E_{21} WAVE

FIG. 3.—Excitation of waves from a coaxial feeder.

design for maximum power transfer has been dealt with
theoretically [110] for the important case, the H_{10} wave,
for which a quarter-wavelength rod placed at a calculable
distance, approximately $\lambda_t/4$, from the closed end of the
guide is satisfactory.

Phase and Group Velocities. The velocity of propagation
of the principal type of guided wave on parallel wire or
coaxial transmission lines of perfect conductivity is equal
to that of light in the medium surrounding the conductors.
In the wave guide this is not so, and we have a case of
normal dispersion, involving both a *phase velocity* and a
group velocity.

The phase velocity is the velocity of propagation of the
surfaces of constant phase—the velocity at which the
patterns of Figure 2 are propagated. These equiphase
surfaces are planes normal to the z-axis, and on any such
plane $\omega t - \beta z = $ constant, and hence $\omega \, dt - \beta \, dz = 0$. Thus
the plane must move forward at a velocity $v' = dz/dt = \omega/\beta$,

which is the phase velocity of the wave. By (1.13) this expression for v' becomes

$$v' = \frac{v}{\sqrt{1 - (f_0/f)^2}}. \qquad \cdots \quad (1.20)$$

Above the critical frequency the phase velocity is greater than the free velocity of light in the medium, v' being infinite at the critical frequency and approaching v as the frequency is increased indefinitely. As v' does not represent the velocity of propagation of energy, the fact that it may exceed the value c does not violate the second relativity postulate.

The concept of phase velocity is valid only for an infinite harmonic wave train. Intelligence is conveyed only by means of finite wave trains which cannot be represented by a single harmonic term such as $\exp i(\omega t - \beta z)$, but a 'signal' of given form can be analysed into a number of infinite trains. For two infinite harmonic wave trains which have slight differences $\delta\omega/2\pi$ and $\delta\beta$ in their frequency and propagation constant, the resultant is

$$\exp i[(\omega - \tfrac{1}{2}\delta\omega)t - (\beta - \tfrac{1}{2}\delta\beta)z]$$
$$+ \exp i[(\omega + \tfrac{1}{2}\delta\omega)t - (\beta + \tfrac{1}{2}\delta\beta)z]$$
$$= 2 \cos \tfrac{1}{2}(t\,\delta\omega - z\,\delta\beta) \exp i(\omega t - \beta z).$$

This represents a wave train of varying amplitude $2 \cos \tfrac{1}{2}(t\,\delta\omega - z\,\delta\beta)$, and the wave appears as a series of moving groups—the 'beats' between the two component waves. The planes of constant group amplitude are defined by $t\,\delta\omega - z\,\delta\beta =$ constant, and thus the groups and the wave energy associated with them are propagated with a velocity $u' = \delta\omega/\delta\beta$. This is the group velocity which, for small values of $\delta\omega$, is approximately $u' = d\omega/d\beta$, and so, from (1.13),

$$u' = \frac{v^2}{v'}. \qquad \cdots \quad (1.21)$$

Since the phase velocity v' is always greater than v, the group velocity u' is always less than v, and becomes zero at the critical frequency. The relations between u', v' and v are shown in Figure 4.

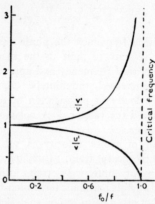

Fig. 4.—Phase and group velocities in a wave guide.
$v = c/(\epsilon\mu)^{\frac{1}{2}}$.

Unless the frequency spectrum of the modulated wave is extremely narrow the group velocity, in cases of dispersion, has no very precise meaning, and the group undergoes increasing deformation as it proceeds.

Longitudinal-section Waves. Since the propagation constants of E and H waves of the same order in m, n are equal, it is possible to produce further wave types by linear superposition of an E_{mn} and an H_{mn} wave. In addition, the relative amplitudes of the two waves can be so chosen that, in the resultant, one of the transverse components of E or H is zero. Then the electric or magnetic vector is confined to one of the planes of longitudinal section of the guide, and hence the waves are called by Buchholz[38] electric and magnetic *Längsschnittwellen* (longitudinal-section waves). They can be derived directly from the fundamental equations (1.3) and (1.4) by putting equal to zero one of the transverse components of E or H. They have the same physical reality as the E and H waves and, like them, can be generated by a suitable arrangement of current-carrying conductors. Longitudinal-section waves are important, as will be seen later, because it is they, and not the E and H waves, which correspond to, and are limiting cases of, the wave types possible in curved and in flared rectangular guides.

The field components for the electric longitudinal-section wave with $E_y = 0$, for example, are derived from equations (1.16) and (1.18) by multiplying by amplitude factors $\dfrac{i\omega\mu}{c}\dfrac{m\pi}{a}$ and $-i\beta\dfrac{n\pi}{b}$ respectively, and adding. The simplest types are those with $m = n = 1$, whose field patterns are shown in Figure 5.

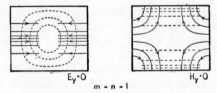

$E_y \cdot 0$ m · n · 1 $H_y \cdot 0$

FIG. 5.—Longitudinal-section waves.

Since any longitudinal-section wave is the resultant of an E and an H wave of the same order, it has the same phase velocity, group velocity, and critical frequency as its components.

Wall Currents. The surface current density K induced in the walls of a guide is at right angles to the tangential magnetic field H_S at the surface and is given in magnitude by the relation $H_S = (4\pi/c)K$. Thus the wall currents form flow patterns orthogonal to the magnetic lines of force, and these are propagated in the direction of the axis at the phase velocity of the wave. In the case of E waves the wall currents all flow parallel to the guide axis.

A narrow slot may be formed in a wall without affecting propagation if the slot does not cut lines of current flow.

Thus longitudinal slots will not disturb E waves. The most important case is the H_{10} wave, and for this the centre line of the broad face is the only position where a longitudinal slot can be cut without interrupting current flow. Such a slot is often used to enable a probe to be moved along a guide in investigations of standing-wave patterns.

Practical Aspects. In practice it is usually important to choose the wave guide dimensions so that only one wave type can be propagated, in order to avoid the simultaneous occurrence of unwanted modes. Obviously the H_{10} mode, in addition to having the lowest critical frequency, has the advantage of having the simplest field configuration, and is therefore used almost exclusively in applications of rectangular wave guides.

If the dimension b for an air-filled guide is made not greater than $\frac{1}{2}a$, then, between excitation wavelength limits of a and $2a$, only the H_{10} mode can be propagated. A larger value of b reduces the range of operation; a smaller value, as will be seen later, increases the losses in the guide. Accordingly, the value of a is usually chosen so that λ is equal to about $4a/3$, with b approximately equal to $\frac{1}{2}a$. Standard sizes are $2 \cdot 84 \times 1 \cdot 34$ inches for 10 cm. wavelength ; $0 \cdot 9 \times 0 \cdot 4$ inches for 3 cm. wavelength. To avoid the possibility of higher-order modes on the one hand and a too close approach to the critical wavelength on the other, it is usual to limit the range of operating wavelength for a particular guide size to about 20 per cent. on either side of the above value of $4a/3$. Standard sizes have been chosen so that these wavebands form an overlapping series.

CHAPTER II

GENERAL TRANSMISSION THEORY

In this chapter we discuss the propagation of electromagnetic waves through tubes of various cross-sections : rectangular, circular, elliptical, and others. The problem is in general to find solutions of Maxwell's equations which are appropriate to the particular form of the bounding surface of the tube, and for each case there will be a particular set of coordinates in which the boundary conditions are most simply expressed. Cartesian coordinates were the obvious choice for a rectangular wave guide ; cylindrical polars are appropriate to the circular cylindrical case. In order to avoid repetition and to secure a unified method of solution, a general treatment of the propagation equations in orthogonal curvilinear coordinates will be made, and from this the several particular cases may be deduced.

ORTHOGONAL CURVILINEAR COORDINATES

Let the Cartesian coordinates x, y, z of a point P be given by the single-valued functions

$$x = f_x(u_1, u_2, u_3), \qquad y = f_y(u_1, u_2, u_3), \qquad z = f_z(u_1, u_2, u_3).$$

Then the position of the point in space is specified when the values of u_1, u_2, u_3 are known. If u_1 is constant, P is restricted to a surface, and its position on that surface is specified by u_2 and u_3. An infinite family of surfaces is produced by giving u_1 successively different values. Application of this process to u_2 and u_3 gives two more

17

families of surfaces. If the surfaces whose parameters are u_1, u_2, and u_3 intersect in the point P, u_1, u_2, and u_3 are called the *curvilinear coordinates* of the point. We shall restrict ourselves to the case in which surfaces of different families intersect at right angles, when the system of coordinates is *orthogonal*. Since u_1, u_2, u_3 will not in general represent distances, the distance ds_1 in Figure 6,

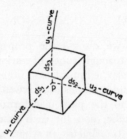

FIG. 6.—Element of volume in curvilinear coordinate system.

between the adjacent points (u_1, u_2, u_3) and $(u_1 + du_1, u_2, u_3)$ is given by du_1 multiplied by a factor h_1. The lengths of the edges of the parallelepiped contained by the surfaces u_1, $u_1 + du_1$, u_2, $u_2 + du_2$, u_3, $u_3 + du_3$ are then

$$ds_1 = h_1 du_1, \qquad ds_2 = h_2 du_2, \qquad ds_3 = h_3 du_3.$$

The factors h_1, h_2, h_3 may vary from point to point in the field and are thus functions of u_1, u_2, u_3. In Cartesian coordinates $h_1 = h_2 = h_3 = 1$. In cylindrical polars ρ, ϕ, z,

$$h_1 du_1 = d\rho, \qquad h_2 du_2 = \rho d\phi, \qquad h_3 du_3 = dz,$$

hence, $\qquad h_1 = 1, \qquad h_2 = \rho, \qquad h_3 = 1.$

In spherical polars r, θ, ϕ,

$$h_1 du_1 = dr, \qquad h_2 du_2 = r d\theta, \qquad h_3 du_3 = r \sin \theta \, d\phi,$$

hence, $\qquad h_1 = 1, \qquad h_2 = r, \qquad h_3 = r \sin \theta.$

We shall require the following two vector differential expressions, in which V is a scalar and A a vector function.[†]

† See, for example, Abraham-Becker, *The Classical Theory of Electricity and Magnetism*, Blackie, 1932 (p. 41).

$$(\text{curl } A)_1 = \frac{1}{h_2 h_3}\left[\frac{\partial(h_3 A_3)}{\partial u_2} - \frac{\partial(h_2 A_2)}{\partial u_3}\right], \text{ \&c.} \quad . \quad . \quad . \quad (2.1)$$

$$\nabla^2 V = \frac{1}{h_1 h_2 h_3}\left[\frac{\partial}{\partial u_1}\left(\frac{h_2 h_3}{h_1}\frac{\partial V}{\partial u_1}\right) + \frac{\partial}{\partial u_2}\left(\frac{h_3 h_1}{h_2}\frac{\partial V}{\partial u_2}\right)\right.$$
$$\left. + \frac{\partial}{\partial u_3}\left(\frac{h_1 h_2}{h_3}\frac{\partial V}{\partial u_3}\right)\right]. \quad (2.2)$$

GENERAL SOLUTION OF ELECTROMAGNETIC EQUATIONS

As before, a dielectric space is postulated, characterized by ε and μ and of zero conductivity. The electric and magnetic field strengths at any point in the dielectric are then determined by the Maxwell field equations (1.1) and (1.2). This dielectric space is bounded by a conducting surface, which will be assumed to possess infinite conductivity and for which the system of coordinates is so chosen that the surface coincides with one or more of the coordinate surfaces.

Elimination of E or H from equations (1.1) shows that both vectors satisfy a vector equation of the form

$$\nabla^2 F - \frac{1}{v^2}\frac{\partial^2 F}{\partial t^2} = 0. \quad . \quad . \quad . \quad (2.3)$$

The first term of this equation is to be interpreted as the Laplacian operating on the *rectangular* components of F. Then each rectangular component of F will satisfy a scalar wave equation of the form

$$\nabla^2 \phi - \frac{1}{v^2}\frac{\partial^2 \phi}{\partial t^2} = 0. \quad . \quad . \quad . \quad (2.4)$$

For all other systems of coordinates, the Laplacian operator, when applied to a vector, operates also upon the unit vectors, and gives rise to a set of three simultaneous partial differential equations whose solution may be very complicated. Thus electromagnetic problems are intrinsically more complex than those of heat conduction or acoustic vibration, which, for all systems of coordinates, depend only on a scalar solution of the wave equation. Vector solutions in terms of general curvilinear coordinates are not known, but for a few special coordinate systems solutions have been found in terms of scalar wave functions with the aid of suitably chosen auxiliary vectors.† Simpler, although less general, methods of solution have been given by Sommerfeld ‡ and by Bromwich [3]. The method of Bromwich will be used here.

Equations (1.1), expanded by (2.1) into their scalar components in terms of curvilinear coordinates, give two triple sets of equations :

$$\frac{i\omega\varepsilon}{c}E_1 = \frac{1}{h_2 h_3}\left[\frac{\partial}{\partial u_2}(h_3 H_3) - \frac{\partial}{\partial u_3}(h_2 H_2)\right]$$

$$\left.\frac{i\omega\varepsilon}{c}E_2 = \frac{1}{h_3 h_1}\left[\frac{\partial}{\partial u_3}(h_1 H_1) - \frac{\partial}{\partial u_1}(h_3 H_3)\right]\right\} \quad . \quad (2.5)$$

$$\frac{i\omega\varepsilon}{c}E_3 = \frac{1}{h_1 h_2}\left[\frac{\partial}{\partial u_1}(h_2 H_2) - \frac{\partial}{\partial u_2}(h_1 H_1)\right],$$

$$-\frac{i\omega\mu}{c}H_1 = \frac{1}{h_2 h_3}\left[\frac{\partial}{\partial u_2}(h_3 E_3) - \frac{\partial}{\partial u_3}(h_2 E_2)\right]$$

$$\left.-\frac{i\omega\mu}{c}H_2 = \frac{1}{h_3 h_1}\left[\frac{\partial}{\partial u_3}(h_1 E_1) - \frac{\partial}{\partial u_1}(h_3 E_3)\right]\right\} \quad . \quad (2.6)$$

$$-\frac{i\omega\mu}{c}H_3 = \frac{1}{h_1 h_2}\left[\frac{\partial}{\partial u_1}(h_2 E_2) - \frac{\partial}{\partial u_2}(h_1 E_1)\right].$$

The general field components can be given in terms of two partial fields, namely, those in which $E_3 = 0$ and $H_3 = 0$

---

† The method is explained in a recent publication : Stratton, *Electromagnetic Theory*, McGraw-Hill, 1941 (Chap. VII).

‡ Riemann-Weber (Frank-v. Mises), *Differentialgleichungen der Physik*, II, Vieweg, 8th edn., 1935 (p. 798).

respectively. Putting first of all $H_3 = 0$, then the last equation of (2.6) gives

$$h_1 E_1 = \frac{\partial P}{\partial u_1}, \qquad h_2 E_2 = \frac{\partial P}{\partial u_2}, \quad . \quad . \quad (2.7)$$

where P is an arbitrary function. Substituting these relations in the first two equations of (2.5) gives

$$\frac{i\omega\varepsilon}{c}\frac{\partial P}{\partial u_1} = -\frac{h_1}{h_2 h_3}\frac{\partial}{\partial u_3}(h_2 H_2), \quad \frac{i\omega\varepsilon}{c}\frac{\partial P}{\partial u_2} = \frac{h_2}{h_3 h_1}\frac{\partial}{\partial u_3}(h_1 H_1). \quad (2.8)$$

The following restrictions are now put on the coordinate system : (1) $h_3 = 1$, (2) h_1/h_2 is a function of u_1 and u_2 only. This permits equations (2.8) to be put in the form

$$\frac{i\omega\varepsilon}{c}\frac{\partial P}{\partial u_1} = -\frac{\partial}{\partial u_3}(h_1 H_2), \quad \frac{i\omega\varepsilon}{c}\frac{\partial P}{\partial u_2} = \frac{\partial}{\partial u_3}(h_2 H_1),$$

and we can then write

$$H_1 = \frac{i\omega\varepsilon}{c}\frac{\partial U}{h_2 \partial u_2}, \qquad H_2 = -\frac{i\omega\varepsilon}{c}\frac{\partial U}{h_1 \partial u_1}, \quad . \quad (2.9)$$

where $P = \partial U/\partial u_3$ defines a function U which is still arbitrary. Substitution from (2.7) and (2.9) in the first two equations of (2.6) gives

$$\frac{\omega^2 \varepsilon\mu}{c^2}\frac{\partial U}{\partial u_2} = \frac{\partial}{\partial u_2}\left(E_3 - \frac{\partial^2 U}{\partial u_3{}^2}\right),$$

$$\frac{\omega^2 \varepsilon\mu}{c^2}\frac{\partial U}{\partial u_1} = \frac{\partial}{\partial u_1}\left(E_3 - \frac{\partial^2 U}{\partial u_3{}^2}\right),$$

which lead to the relation

$$E_3 = \frac{\partial^2 U}{\partial u_3{}^2} + \frac{\omega^2}{v^2}U. \quad . \quad . \quad . \quad (2.10)$$

Lastly, substitution for E_3, H_1 and H_2 in the third equation of (2.5) gives the differential equation to be satisfied by U,

$$\frac{1}{h_1 h_2}\left[\frac{\partial}{\partial u_1}\left(\frac{h_2}{h_1}\frac{\partial U}{\partial u_1}\right) + \frac{\partial}{\partial u_2}\left(\frac{h_1}{h_2}\frac{\partial U}{\partial u_2}\right)\right] + \frac{\partial^2 U}{\partial u_3{}^2} + \frac{\omega^2}{v^2}U = 0. \quad (2.11)$$

The complete set of components for this first partial field is then

$$E_1 = \frac{1}{h_1} \frac{\partial^2 U}{\partial u_3 \partial u_1} \qquad H_1 = \frac{i\omega\varepsilon}{c} \frac{\partial U}{h_2 \partial u_2}$$

$$E_2 = \frac{1}{h_2} \frac{\partial^2 U}{\partial u_3 \partial u_2} \qquad H_2 = -\frac{i\omega\varepsilon}{c} \frac{\partial U}{h_1 \partial u_1}$$

$$E_3 = \frac{\partial^2 U}{\partial u_3{}^2} + \frac{\omega^2}{v^2} U \qquad H_3 = 0.$$
$$(2.12)$$

Similarly, by putting $E_3 = 0$, the components of the second solution are found to be

$$E_1 = -\frac{i\omega\mu}{c} \frac{\partial V}{h_2 \partial u_2} \qquad H_1 = \frac{1}{h_1} \frac{\partial^2 V}{\partial u_3 \partial u_1}$$

$$E_2 = \frac{i\omega\mu}{c} \frac{\partial V}{h_1 \partial u_1} \qquad H_2 = \frac{1}{h_2} \frac{\partial^2 V}{\partial u_3 \partial u_2}$$

$$E_3 = 0 \qquad H_3 = \frac{\partial^2 V}{\partial u_3{}^2} + \frac{\omega^2}{v^2} V.$$
$$(2.13)$$

where V satisfies the same equation, (2.11), as does U. The general solution is obtained by superposing these two particular solutions. They correspond to the solutions for E and H waves obtained for the rectangular wave guide.

Comparison with the derivation given by Sommerfeld †
shows that U and V are the scalar values of the electric and magnetic Hertzian vectors directed along the u_3-axis. Any field of force derivable from the electric Hertzian vector can be shown to be due to a distribution of electric dipoles, while one dependent on the magnetic Hertzian vector has its origin in a system of magnetic dipoles. Thus E and H waves can be generated by exciter systems which are equivalent to electric and magnetic oscillating dipoles respectively. A short linear conductor placed along the u_3-axis, and a small closed loop of wire set with its plane

† Riemann-Weber, *loc. cit.*

normal to the u_3-axis, are simple examples of the two forms of exciter.

It is to be observed, by comparison with (2.2), that equation (2.11), which corresponds to equation (1.7) in Chapter I and determines the form of the solutions, is not *in general* a wave equation $\{\nabla^2 + (\omega/v)^2\}U = 0$. In the particular cases to be dealt with here, either it is a wave equation identically, or it can be reduced to one by simple transformation. The method of solution of the wave equation (2.4) is by ' separation of the variables ', ϕ being expressed in the form $\phi = f_1(u_1)f_2(u_2)f_3(u_3)$. The equation is thereby split up into three parts, each involving only one variable and solvable separately.

If u_1 = const. is the equation of the bounding surface, E_2 and E_3 will require to be zero for that value of u_1, since they are then tangential to the boundary. From (2.12) and (2.13) can be seen the conditions then to be satisfied, viz., for the first solution, $[U]_{u_1=\text{const.}} = 0$; for the second, $[\partial V/\partial u_1]_{u_1=\text{const.}} = 0$.

For a rectangular wave guide Cartesian coordinates are used, and the solution of (2.11) is chosen so that there are standing waves in the x- and y-directions, and a progressive wave in the z-direction. Thus

$$U, V = \frac{\sin}{\cos} k_1 x \frac{\sin}{\cos} k_2 y \, e^{-\gamma z},$$

and from this the two solutions found in Chapter I are obtained.

CIRCULAR WAVE GUIDES

We now take up the particular case of the wave guide whose boundary is a circular cylinder, of infinite axial length, composed by a perfect conductor surrounding a perfect dielectric. This form was investigated by Rayleigh [2] in 1897, and has been treated in greater detail by Barrow [18], and Carson, Mead and Schelkunoff [20].

The coordinates which are appropriate here are cylindrical polars ρ, ϕ, z, the z-axis being the axis of the cylinder.

Then, if these replace u_1, u_2, u_3 respectively, $h_1 = 1$, $h_2 = \rho$, $h_3 = 1$, and the conditions which were required in obtaining the general solution, viz. $h_3 = 1$, h_1/h_2 a function of u_1 and u_2 only, are satisfied. When these values are substituted in equation (2.11) it becomes

$$\frac{1}{\rho}\frac{\partial}{\partial\rho}\left(\rho\frac{\partial U}{\partial\rho}\right) + \frac{1}{\rho^2}\frac{\partial^2 U}{\partial\phi^2} + \frac{\partial^2 U}{\partial z^2} + \frac{\omega^2}{v^2}U = 0. \quad (2.14)$$

This is the wave equation in cylindrical coordinates, and is solved by assuming a solution of the form $U = R\Phi Z$, where R, Φ, and Z are respectively functions of ρ, ϕ, and z only. The equation then splits up into three parts, each containing only one coordinate. For a progressive wave in the z-direction and a standing wave along the ϕ-coordinate, the complete solution is obtained :

$$U = \left\{\begin{matrix} J_n(k\rho) \\ Y_n(k\rho) \end{matrix}\right\} \begin{matrix} \cos \\ \sin \end{matrix} n\phi\, e^{-\gamma z}, \quad . \quad . \quad (2.15)$$

where $J_n(x)$ and $Y_n(x)$ are Bessel functions of the first and second kinds of order n, solutions of Bessel's equation

$$\frac{d^2 y}{dx^2} + \frac{1}{x}\frac{dy}{dx} + \left(1 - \frac{n^2}{x^2}\right)y = 0,$$

γ is determined by the relation

$$k^2 = (\omega/v)^2 + \gamma^2, \quad . \quad . \quad . \quad (2.16)$$

and n is at present arbitrary. Two sets of electric and magnetic field components are derived from this solution by means of (2.12) and (2.13). These fields have H_z and E_z zero respectively ; therefore the first is a transverse magnetic or E wave, and the second a transverse electric or H wave.

E Waves. The Bessel function of the second kind is not valid for hollow cylinders, since it becomes infinite for $\rho = 0$, and the field must be finite at all points. By suitable choice of the zero of the ϕ-coordinate the expression for U may be simplified to

$$U = J_n(k\rho) \cos n\phi\, e^{-\gamma z}. \quad . \quad . \quad (2.17)$$

In order that the field may be continuous, the cosine term must be of period 2π, and the values of n are therefore restricted to integral values or zero. The necessary and sufficient boundary condition is that U should be zero at the tube surface $\rho = a$. This condition provides the equation

$$J_n(ka) = 0, \quad . \quad . \quad . \quad . \quad (2.18)$$

which determines values of k and hence of the propagation constant γ. Equation (2.18) has an infinite number of real roots determining an infinite number of possible waves. Of these waves only a finite number will be unattenuated, since for free transmission γ must be a pure imaginary, and so, k being real, the frequency must be so high that, by (2.16),

$$\omega/v > k.$$

The characteristic values of k will be denoted by k_{nm}, where $k_{nm}a$ is the mth root of $J_n(ka)$, and these will define waves of the type E_{nm}. Each wave type thus has a critical frequency below which its free propagation is not possible, and these frequencies are given for the various values of k by the equation

$$f_0 = \frac{ck}{2\pi(\varepsilon\mu)^{\frac{1}{2}}} \quad . \quad . \quad . \quad . \quad (2.19)$$

Above the critical frequency the real and imaginary parts of the propagation constant are

$$\alpha = 0, \qquad \beta = \left[\frac{\omega^2}{v^2} - k^2\right]^{\frac{1}{2}}, \quad . \quad . \quad (2.20)$$

and hence the wavelength in the tube, λ_t, is given by

$$\frac{1}{\lambda_t} = \frac{\beta}{2\pi} = \left[\frac{1}{\lambda^2} - \left(\frac{k}{2\pi}\right)^2\right]^{\frac{1}{2}}, \quad . \quad . \quad (2.21)$$

λ being the wavelength of the oscillation in the *unbounded* dielectric. The value of λ at the critical frequency is given by

$$\lambda_0 = \frac{2\pi}{k}, \quad . \quad . \quad . \quad . \quad (2.22)$$

3

and the expression for λ_t can be put in the form

$$\frac{1}{\lambda_t} = \left[\frac{1}{\lambda^2} - \frac{1}{\lambda_0^2}\right]^{\frac{1}{2}} \quad . \quad . \quad . \quad . \quad (2.23)$$

As the excitation wavelength approaches the critical wavelength, λ_t approaches infinity.

Calculation of the field components from equation (2.12) gives

$$\left.\begin{aligned}
E_z &= k^2 J_n(k\rho) \cos n\phi \, e^{-i\beta z} \\
E_\rho &= - i\beta k \, J_n'(k\rho) \cos n\phi \, e^{-i\beta z} \\
E_\phi &= \frac{i\beta n}{\rho} J_n(k\rho) \sin n\phi \, e^{-i\beta z} \\
H_z &= 0 \\
H_\rho &= - \frac{i\omega\varepsilon n}{\rho c} J_n(k\rho) \sin n\phi \, e^{-i\beta z} \\
H_\phi &= - \frac{i\omega\varepsilon k}{c} J_n'(k\rho) \cos n\phi \, e^{-i\beta z}.
\end{aligned}\right\} \quad . \quad (2.24)$$

The prime on the Bessel functions denotes differentiation with respect to the argument $k\rho$.

H Waves. The set of field components for H waves is determined from equation (2.13), using (2.17) to define V :

$$\left.\begin{aligned}
H_z &= k^2 J_n(k\rho) \cos n\phi \, e^{-i\beta z} \\
H_\rho &= - i\beta k \, J_n'(k\rho) \cos n\phi \, e^{-i\beta z} \\
H_\phi &= \frac{i\beta n}{\rho} J_n(k\rho) \sin n\phi \, e^{-i\beta z} \\
E_z &= 0 \\
E_\rho &= \frac{i\omega\mu n}{\rho c} J_n(k\rho) \sin n\phi \, e^{-i\beta z} \\
E_\phi &= \frac{i\omega\mu k}{c} J_n'(k\rho) \cos n\phi \, e^{-i\beta z}.
\end{aligned}\right\} \quad . \quad (2.25)$$

Since E_z is already zero, the boundary condition remaining is that E_ϕ should be zero at $\rho = a$, where it is tangential to the tube wall. The condition for this, which determines k, is

$$J_n'(ka) = 0, \quad \ldots \quad \ldots \quad (2.26)$$

and, with values of k thus determined, the propagation constants, critical frequencies, &c., are given as before by (2.19) to (2.23).†

As with rectangular guides, for both E and H waves in hollow circular cylinders the phase velocity v' is greater than that of light in the unbounded medium and is given by

$$v' = \frac{\omega}{\beta} = \frac{v}{\sqrt{1 - (f_0/f)^2}}. \quad \ldots \quad (2.27)$$

The group velocity u', the velocity of energy transmission, is related to v' by the expression

$$u' = \frac{d\omega}{d\beta} = \frac{v^2}{v'}. \quad \ldots \quad \ldots \quad (2.28)$$

PROPERTIES OF THE WAVE TYPES

The roots of the equation $J_n(x) = 0$ are contained in many collections of tables ‡; a comprehensive list of roots of $J_n'(x) = 0$ and of $J_n(x) = 0$ has been given by Wilson, Schramm, and Kinzer.[90] Table 1 gives some of the roots of these two equations. Often the subscript indicating the value of m is omitted, and m is then understood to have the value 1.

Some values of critical wavelength in terms of the tube radius, calculated from the table on page 28, are

E_0, $2 \cdot 61a$; E_1, $1 \cdot 64a$; H_0, $1 \cdot 64a$; H_1, $3 \cdot 41a$.

The lines of electric force for the various wave types may be plotted from solutions of the equation

$$\frac{d\rho}{E_\rho} = \frac{\rho d\phi}{E_\phi} = \frac{dz}{E_z},$$

† In finding numerical values of λ_t from (2.23) the tables of electronic functions in *Miscellaneous Physical Tables*, W.P.A., New York, 1941, are most useful.

‡ e.g. Jahnke-Emde, *Tables of Functions*, Teubner, Leipzig, 1938.

TABLE I

	E wave. $J_n(ka) = 0$.			H wave. $J_n'(ka) = 0$.		
n	$k_{n1}a$	$k_{n2}a$	$k_{n3}a$	$k_{n1}a$	$k_{n2}a$	$k_{n3}a$
0	2·405	5·520	8·654	3·832	7·016	10·173
1	3·832	7·016	10·173	1·841	5·331	8·536
2	5·136	8·417	11·620	3·054	6·706	9·969

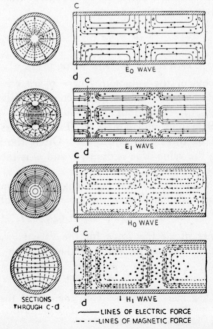

E_0 WAVE

E_1 WAVE

H_0 WAVE

H_1 WAVE

SECTIONS THROUGH c-d

—— LINES OF ELECTRIC FORCE
--- --- LINES OF MAGNETIC FORCE

FIG. 7.—Lines of force of waves in a circular guide (Southworth[19]).

and Figure 7 shows some of these fields. The value of n gives the number of electric or magnetic nodal diametral lines in a transverse section of the field, while on the order m of the zero depends the number of concentric nodal circles.

WAVES WITH E_z AND H_z ZERO

The particular solution, mentioned in Chapter I, in which both E_z and H_z are zero will now be considered. If in the solution (2.12) $E_3 \equiv 0$, then U must satisfy two equations,

$$\frac{\partial^2 U}{\partial u_3^2} + \frac{\omega^2}{v^2} U = 0 \quad . \quad . \quad . \quad (2.29)$$

and

$$\frac{\partial}{\partial u_1}\left(\frac{h_2}{h_1}\frac{\partial U}{\partial u_1}\right) + \frac{\partial}{\partial u_2}\left(\frac{h_1}{h_2}\frac{\partial U}{\partial u_2}\right) = 0. \quad . \quad . \quad (2.30)$$

The first of these gives a propagation constant $\gamma = 0 + i\omega/v$. The second is the Laplace equation for two dimensions, and thus U is a two-dimensional potential function. The function must be constant over the equipotential which coincides with the boundary surface, and, if this does not enclose any electric charge, the field is zero at every point inside the surface. Hence no wave having both E_z and H_z zero is possible in a hollow tube. If, however, there is another metallic boundary inside the tube, U is constant on each, and a potential gradient may exist between them. The solution of (2.30) for two coaxial cylinders is

$$U = (A \log \rho + B)e^{-i\omega z/v}.$$

Replacing A by $-1/\gamma$, the field given by (2.12) becomes

$$E_\rho = (\mu/\varepsilon)^{\frac{1}{2}}H_\phi = \frac{1}{\rho}e^{-i\omega z/v}, \quad . \quad . \quad . \quad (2.31)$$

which are the familiar equations for the principal wave in the coaxial line, allowing free propagation at all frequencies. This relationship between wave guides and coaxial lines was pointed out by Clavier [23].

OTHER SECTIONS BOUNDED BY CIRCULAR CYLINDERS

If the cylinder is not complete, but is in the form of a wedge of angle ϕ_0 bounded by two axial planes and a cylinder of radius a as shown in cross-section in Figure 8(a),

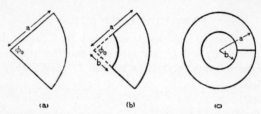

FIG. 8.—Cross-sections of tubes bounded by cylinders.

the form of the solution will be similar to that for the complete cylinder, but now the order of the Bessel function will not be in general integral. The appropriate form of the function U for an E wave is now

$$U = J_p(k\rho)(A \cos p\phi + B \sin p\phi) e^{-\gamma z},$$

with the boundary conditions that U is zero for $\phi = 0$, ϕ_0 and $\rho = a$. These give

$$U = J_p(k\rho) \sin p\phi \, e^{-\gamma z}, \quad . \quad . \quad . \quad (2.32)$$

where $p = n\pi/\phi_0$, $n = 1, 2, 3, \ldots$, and k is a solution of $J_p(ka) = 0$. For H waves the function is

$$V = J_p(k\rho) \cos p\phi \, e^{-\gamma z}, \quad . \quad . \quad . \quad (2.33)$$

where $p = n\pi/\phi_0$, $n = 0, 1, 2, \ldots$, and k is a solution of $J_p'(ka) = 0$. If $\phi_0 = \pi$ the solutions become those for waves in the complete cylinder (excluding the E_0 wave). Thus a circular wave guide can be divided into two semicylinders without affecting the transmission of any but E_0 waves.

For a tube formed by two axial planes and two coaxial cylinders as shown in Figure 8 (b), the Bessel function of the second kind can appear in the solution, since now $\rho = 0$ is excluded from the region. Then we have

$$U, V = [A J_p(k\rho) + B Y_p(k\rho)](C \cos p\phi + D \sin p\phi)e^{-\gamma z}. \quad (2.34)$$

The values of p are determined from the wedge angle as before. Also either U or $\partial V/\partial \rho$ must vanish at $\rho = a$ and $\rho = b$. A non-trivial solution requires either

$$\frac{J_p(ka)}{Y_p(ka)} = \frac{J_p(kb)}{Y_p(kb)} \text{ or } \frac{J_p{}'(ka)}{Y_p{}'(ka)} = \frac{J_p{}'(kb)}{Y_p{}'(kb)}, \quad (2.35)$$

the first equation determining values of k for E waves, and the second for H waves. If $\phi_0 = 2\pi$ and there are no partitions between the cylinders, p becomes zero or an integer, and equations (2.35) determine modes of wave transmission in the coaxial line. These modes were called by Carson [26] *complementary*, as opposed to the *principal* type already discussed in which both E_z and H_z are zero.

Some roots of equations (2.35) are given in the tables of Jahnke-Emde. A more comprehensive set of solutions has been given by Dwight [121], and graphical values by Bondi and Kuhn [76].

An interesting case discussed by Barrow and Schaevitz [14] is that of the so-called septate coaxial cable, shown in section in Figure 8 (c), which can be regarded as a rectangular guide rolled up into a cylinder. The longest critical wavelength in a rectangular guide of sides a and b $(a > b)$ is $2a$. Thus in the septate coaxial line a wave type is to be expected, whose critical wavelength is approximately twice the mean circumference of the two cylinders. This wave does exist, and is the simplest H type given by (2.35) with $p = \frac{1}{2}$. Its critical wavelength is considerably longer than that of any wave type in a hollow tube of the same outer dimensions, the actual value lying between the limits $4\pi a$, when $b = a$, and $2\pi a/1\cdot 17$, when $b = 0$.

DIELECTRIC GUIDES

Waves may also be guided along a dielectric cylinder bounded externally by a medium of smaller dielectric constant. The theory of such *dielectric guides* was given by Hondros and Debye [28], and confirmed experimentally by Schriever [30]. The method of attack is similar to that used in the previous sections, but the more complex boundary conditions make calculation of characteristic values laborious. There are E and H waves similar to those inside conducting tubes, but one of each type must normally be superposed to satisfy the boundary conditions; only in the case of E_0 and H_0 waves can the two types exist separately. The lines of force now extend from the inner dielectric into the surrounding space, and the wave energy is divided between the two regions. For high values of the dielectric constant of the inner medium and for frequencies well above the critical value the energy travels predominantly in the inner dielectric, and the velocity of propagation is approximately equal to the velocity of light in this medium. At frequencies near the critical value and when the two values of dielectric constant are nearly equal much of the energy travels in the external dielectric, with a velocity approaching that of light in the external medium.

For the E_0 wave the critical frequency is given by

$$f_0 = \frac{ck}{2\pi\sqrt{\varepsilon_1\mu_1 - \varepsilon_2\mu_2}}, \text{ (cf. 2.19)} \quad . \quad (2.36)$$

where the suffixes 1 and 2 refer to the inner and outer media whose radius of separation is a, and ka has the value 2·405 as for the hollow metal wave guide. Thus, for instance, the critical free-space wavelength for a cylinder of water ($\varepsilon_1 = 81$) of radius 1 cm., surrounded by air, is about 23 cm.

An interesting comparison has been made by Droste [9]

of the characteristics of wave propagation in a conductor surrounded by a dielectric, a dielectric surrounded by a different dielectric, and a dielectric surrounded by a conductor.

ELLIPTIC WAVE GUIDES

We shall now consider briefly wave propagation through a cylinder of elliptical cross-section. Such a shape is unlikely to be used in practice, but the analysis, which is due to Brillouin [7] and Chu [33], is useful in determining the stability of the various waveforms in the circular cylinder under slight deformations of the tube. This will be discussed in a later chapter.

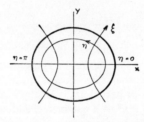

FIG. 9.—Coordinate system for elliptic cylinder.

For an elliptical boundary the use of plane confocal coordinates ξ, η, z is appropriate (Figure 9), these being defined in terms of Cartesians by the relations

$$x = g \cosh \xi \cos \eta, \quad y = g \sinh \xi \sin \eta, \quad z = z.$$

The surfaces of constant ξ are confocal elliptic cylinders, and those of constant η confocal hyperbolic cylinders, which cut the ξ-surfaces orthogonally, both having common foci at $x = \pm g$, $y = 0$. The z-axis of coordinates coincides with the axis of the tube, and one of the elliptic cylinder surfaces $\xi = \xi_0$ coincides with the inner surface of the tube. The major and minor semi-axes of the tube are then given by $g \cosh \xi_0$ and $g \sinh \xi_0$ respectively, and its eccentricity by $1/\cosh \xi_0$. If ξ, η, z replace the curvilinear coordinates u_1, u_2, u_3, the local units of length are

$$h_1 = h_2 = g(\cosh^2 \xi - \cos^2 \eta)^{\frac{1}{2}}, \; h_3 = 1.$$

Substitution in (2.11) gives the equation

$$\frac{\partial^2 U}{\partial \xi^2} + \frac{\partial^2 U}{\partial \eta^2} + g^2(\cosh^2 \xi - \cos^2 \eta)\left[\frac{\partial^2 U}{\partial z^2} + \frac{\omega^2}{v^2} U\right] = 0, \; . \quad (2.37)$$

of which the solution, found by separating the variables,

is $\qquad U = ce_n(i\xi, q)\, ce_n(\eta, q)\, e^{-\gamma z}$
or $\qquad U = se_n(i\xi, q)\, se_n(\eta, q)\, e^{-\gamma z}.$ $\left.\begin{array}{c} \\ \end{array}\right\}$ . . . (2.38)

The functions $ce_n(x, q)$ and $se_n(x, q)$ are the even and odd Mathieu functions, periodic solutions of Mathieu's equation [120]

$$\frac{d^2 y}{dx^2} + (G + 16q \cos 2x)y = 0, \; . \quad . \quad . \quad (2.39)$$

where $q = -g^2 k^2/32$ and, as in the preceding sections, $k^2 = \omega^2/v^2 + \gamma^2$. The separation constant G is determined by the condition that the solution must, in order to be single-valued, be of period 2π. All the Mathieu functions in (2.38) contain $g^2 k^2$ as a parameter, and so the boundary conditions provide characteristic values of k^2 and hence of γ. For E waves the boundary condition $U = 0$ around the ellipse $\xi = \xi_0$, gives

$$ce_n(i\xi_0, q) = 0 \text{ or } se_n(i\xi_0, q) = 0, \; . \quad . \quad (2.40)$$

and for H waves, $\partial V/\partial \xi_0 = 0$, where $V = U$,

$$\frac{\partial}{\partial \xi_0} ce_n(i\xi_0, q) = 0 \quad \text{or} \quad \frac{\partial}{\partial \xi_0} se_n(i\xi_0, q) = 0. \quad . \quad (2.41)$$

The Mathieu functions are considerably more complex than Bessel functions, and no complete tables are yet available. The references quoted may be consulted for details of approximation methods of determining propagation constants. Wave types are characterized by indices c,n or s,n to indicate dependence on the functions ce_n or se_n. n having an integral value, and an index m

to indicate the order of the root. This yields waves of the types E_{cnm}, E_{snm}, H_{cnm} and H_{snm}. Since ce_n and se_n are even and odd functions respectively, the corresponding

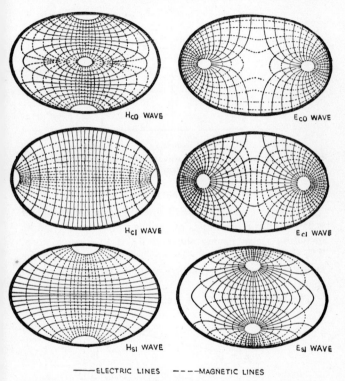

H_{c0} WAVE

E_{c0} WAVE

H_{c1} WAVE

E_{c1} WAVE

H_{s1} WAVE

E_{s1} WAVE

——ELECTRIC LINES   ————MAGNETIC LINES

FIG. 10.—Lines of force of waves in an elliptic guide.

waves may be called even and odd, and e and o may replace c and s as subscripts. For waves of zero order, only the even type occurs, since se_0 does not exist. Figures 10 and 11, taken from Chu's paper [33], show some field configurations which have been computed, and the variation of critical wavelength with eccentricity.

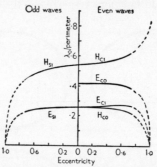

FIG. 11.—Variation of critical wavelength with eccentricity of an elliptic tube of constant perimeter.

SECTORAL HORN

In a later chapter we shall investigate the radiation of waves from the open ends of various forms of wave guide, including those having the end flared to form a horn. The propagation of waves inside such horns will be considered here, and the first example is one of sectoral shape.

The horn, Figure 12, is enclosed by the surfaces given

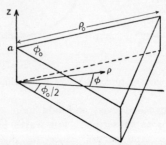

FIG. 12.—Coordinate system for sectoral horn.

in cylindrical polars by $\phi = \pm\, \phi_0/2$, $z = 0, a$. The sides of the horn are assumed to extend to infinity in the ρ-direction, which means in practice that end effects due to a finite length of horn are neglected. Since the field is to be expressed in cylindrical polar coordinates the equation to be solved for U is the equation (2.14) already considered. However, propagation is now in the direction of ρ, and so a standing wave form will be chosen for the variation with the z-coordinate, giving

$$U = H_p^{(2)}(k\rho) \begin{matrix} \cos \\ \sin \end{matrix} p\phi \begin{matrix} \cos \\ \sin \end{matrix} qz, \quad \cdot \quad \cdot \quad (2.42)$$

where $k^2 = \omega^2/v^2 - q^2$. For waves whose variation *in the direction of propagation* is characterized by a solution of Bessel's equation, we use, in place of the functions J_p and Y_p, the Hankel function of the second kind $H_p^{(2)}$, which is defined by the relation $H_p^{(2)} = J_p - i\, Y_p$. That this represents a travelling wave is evident from the fact that for large values of ρ the asymptotic representation for the Hankel function is

$$H_p^{(2)}(k\rho) \longrightarrow \sqrt{\frac{2}{\pi k \rho}}\, e^{-i\left(k\rho - \frac{2p+1}{4}\pi\right)}. \quad \cdot \quad (2.43)$$

The corresponding representation for $J_p(k\rho)$ is

$$J_p(k\rho) \longrightarrow \sqrt{\frac{2}{\pi k \rho}} \cos\left(k\rho - \frac{2p+1}{4}\pi\right), \quad \cdot \quad (2.44)$$

and thus these two correspond to the functions $e^{-i\beta z}$ and $\cos \beta z$ which in previous cases represented travelling and stationary waves respectively.[†]

The values of p and q in (2.42) are determined by the conditions that the component E_ρ, derived from U, is zero at the bounding surfaces. The two solutions (2.12) and (2.13) give waves with $H_z = 0$ and $E_z = 0$, but as

[†] Sommerfeld in Riemann-Weber, *loc. cit.* (p. 836).

the z-axis is not the direction of propagation these are not what have been defined as E and H waves. They are the counterpart in the sectoral horn of the longitudinal-section waves possible in a rectangular wave guide. To produce solutions with $H_\rho = 0$ or $E_\rho = 0$ a cyclic interchange of the coordinates to ϕ, z, ρ would be necessary, but then $h_1 = \rho$, $h_2 = 1$, and this infringes the requirement that h_1/h_2 should be a function of u_1 and u_2 only.

The most important practical case is that in which $H_z = 0$ and $q = 0$. The term $\sin p\phi$ in U will be dropped so that the field may have symmetry about the central plane and hence produce a radiated beam with a central lobe. The field components derived from (2.12) are then

$$\left.\begin{aligned}
E_\rho &= E_\phi = H_z = 0 \\
E_z &= H_{n\pi/\phi_0}^{(2)}\left(\frac{\omega}{v}\rho\right) \cos\frac{n\pi\phi}{\phi_0} \\
H_\rho &= \frac{n\pi c}{i\omega\mu\rho\phi_0} H_{n\pi/\phi_0}^{(2)}\left(\frac{\omega}{v}\rho\right) \sin\frac{n\pi\phi}{\phi_0} \\
H_\phi &= -i\sqrt{\frac{\varepsilon}{\mu}} H_{n\pi/\phi_0}^{(2)'}\left(\frac{\omega}{v}\rho\right) \cos\frac{n\pi\phi}{\phi_0},
\end{aligned}\right\} \quad . \quad (2.45)$$

n having the values 1, 3, 5, . . . Since $E_\rho = 0$, this is a true H wave, and the arrangement of its field components makes it the counterpart in a sectoral horn of an H_{n0} wave in a rectangular tube. Figure 13 is a representation of the lines of force of this wave for $n = 1$. Barrow and Chu [35] extend to this case the definition of propagation constant for transmission lines, i.e. $\gamma = \alpha + i\beta = -(\partial/\partial x) \log E$, using for E the component E_z and replacing x by ρ; then $\gamma = -(\omega/v)H_{n\pi/\phi_0}^{(2)'}(\omega\rho/v)/H_{n\pi/\phi_0}^{(2)}(\omega\rho/v)$. With the aid of asymptotic expressions for the Hankel function they show that the interior of the horn can be divided into an *attenuation region* and a *transmission region*. The attenuation region extends out from the apex, and there

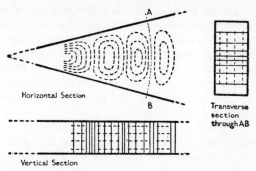

FIG. 13.—Field of H_{10} wave in a sectoral horn.

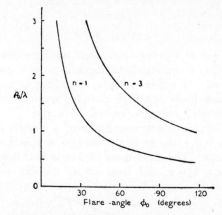

FIG. 14.—Dividing line between attenuation and transmission regions in the sectoral horn.

the attenuation constant is high and the phase constant small compared with their free-space values. This region merges into the transmission region, which extends back from the mouth of the horn, and in which attenuation is small and the phase constant approaches its free-space value. As the angle of flare increases, the extent of the attenuation region decreases. A convenient, but arbitrary, dividing line between the two regions—which by their nature are not sharply defined—is given by the values of ρ for which $Y_{n\pi/\phi_0}(\omega\rho/v)$ has its first zero. Figure 14 shows these values, expressed in units of wavelength, for varying flare angle. They are calculated from data in the tables of Jahnke and Emde.

If p in (2.42) is put equal to zero, another H wave is obtained which is the equivalent of an H_{0n} wave in a rectangular guide. This has a critical wavelength given by $\lambda_0 = 2a/n$, which is in contrast with the H_{n0} type first discussed for which there is no definite critical wavelength. No E-type waves exist in a sectoral horn.

CONICAL HORN

If the end of a circular cylindrical wave guide be flared into a cone, a conical electromagnetic horn is produced. By the use of spherical polar coordinates, modes of propagation in an infinitely extended horn of this form can be derived from the general equations.

When the curvilinear coordinates u_1, u_2, u_3 are replaced by polars θ, ϕ, r, the surface of the cone is given by $\theta = \frac{1}{2}\theta_0$ (Figure 15). The local units of length are then $h_1 = r$, $h_2 = r\sin\theta$, $h_3 = 1$, and these satisfy the two necessary

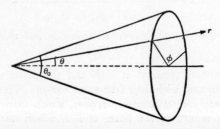

FIG. 15.—Coordinate system for conical horn.

conditions. In polar coordinates the equation for U, (2.11), becomes

$$\frac{1}{r^2 \sin \theta} \left[\frac{\partial}{\partial \theta} \left(\sin \theta \frac{\partial U}{\partial \theta} \right) + \frac{1}{\sin \theta} \frac{\partial^2 U}{\partial \phi^2} \right]$$

$$+ \frac{\partial^2 U}{\partial r^2} + \frac{\omega^2}{v^2} U = 0. \quad . \quad . \quad . \quad (2.46)$$

That this is not a wave equation will be seen by expanding $\nabla^2 U$ in spherical coordinates by (2.2); but, after the simple transformation $U = rF$, F is found to satisfy the wave equation $\nabla^2 F + (\omega/v)^2 F = 0$. The wave function appropriate to the conditions of the problem is shown † by separation of the variables to be

$$F = r^{-\frac{1}{2}} H_{n+\frac{1}{2}}^{(2)} \left(\frac{\omega}{v} r \right) P_n^m (\cos \theta) \cos m\phi. \quad . \quad (2.47)$$

The last two terms in the expression form a tesseral harmonic of degree n, $P_n^m(\cos \theta)$ being a solution of Legendre's associated equation

$$(1 - \eta^2) \frac{d^2 y}{d\eta^2} - 2\eta \frac{dy}{d\eta} + \left[n(n + 1) - \frac{m^2}{1 - \eta^2} \right] y = 0,$$

in which $\eta = \cos \theta$. The second solution of this equation, $Q_n^m(\eta)$, must be excluded from physical fields in a region which includes $\eta = \pm 1$, because of its singularities there.

The two classes of wave derived from F are true E and H waves, having $H_\rho = 0$ and $E_\rho = 0$ respectively. For continuity of field $\cos m\phi$ must be of period 2π, so that m is restricted to zero or integral values. The boundary conditions determine non-integral values of n which make E_r and E_ϕ zero at the surface $\theta = \frac{1}{2}\theta_0$. Thus n is determined for E waves from the equation $P_n^m(\cos \frac{1}{2}\theta_0) = 0$, and for H waves from $(d/d\theta_0)P_n^m(\cos \frac{1}{2}\theta_0) = 0$. The sets

† Riemann-Weber, *loc. cit.* (p. 872).

4

of field equations derived through $U = V = rF$ from (2.12) and (2.13) are:

E wave

$$E_r = \frac{n(n+1)}{r^{\frac{3}{2}}} H_{n+\frac{1}{2}}^{(2)}\left(\frac{\omega}{v}r\right) P_n^m(\cos\theta)\cos m\phi$$

$$E_\theta = \frac{1}{r}\frac{d}{dr}\left[r^{\frac{1}{2}}H_{n+\frac{1}{2}}^{(2)}\left(\frac{\omega}{v}r\right)\right]\frac{d}{d\theta}P_n^m(\cos\theta)\cos m\phi$$

$$E_\phi = -\frac{m}{r\sin\theta}\frac{d}{dr}\left[r^{\frac{1}{2}}H_{n+\frac{1}{2}}^{(2)}\left(\frac{\omega}{v}r\right)\right]P_n^m(\cos\theta)\sin m\phi \qquad (2.48)$$

$$H_r = 0$$

$$H_\theta = -\frac{i\omega\varepsilon m}{cr^{\frac{1}{2}}\sin\theta}H_{n+\frac{1}{2}}^{(2)}\left(\frac{\omega}{v}r\right)P_n^m(\cos\theta)\sin m\phi$$

$$H_\phi = -\frac{i\omega\varepsilon}{cr^{\frac{1}{2}}}H_{n+\frac{1}{2}}^{(2)}\left(\frac{\omega}{v}r\right)\frac{d}{d\theta}P_n^m(\cos\theta)\cos m\phi ;$$

H wave

$$E_r = 0$$

$$E_\theta = \frac{i\omega\mu m}{cr^{\frac{1}{2}}\sin\theta}H_{n+\frac{1}{2}}^{(2)}\left(\frac{\omega}{v}r\right)P_n^m(\cos\theta)\sin m\phi$$

$$E_\phi = \frac{i\omega\mu}{cr^{\frac{1}{2}}}H_{n+\frac{1}{2}}^{(2)}\left(\frac{\omega}{v}r\right)\frac{d}{d\theta}P_n^m(\cos\theta)\cos m\phi$$

$$H_r = \frac{n(n+1)}{r^{\frac{3}{2}}}H_{n+\frac{1}{2}}^{(2)}\left(\frac{\omega}{v}r\right)P_n^m(\cos\theta)\cos m\phi \qquad (2.49)$$

$$H_\theta = \frac{1}{r}\frac{d}{dr}\left[r^{\frac{1}{2}}H_{n+\frac{1}{2}}^{(2)}\left(\frac{\omega}{v}r\right)\right]\frac{d}{d\theta}P_n^m(\cos\theta)\cos m\phi$$

$$H_\phi = -\frac{m}{r\sin\theta}\frac{d}{dr}\left[r^{\frac{1}{2}}H_{n+\frac{1}{2}}^{(2)}\left(\frac{\omega}{v}r\right)\right]P_n^m(\cos\theta)\sin m\phi.$$

As with the sectoral horn, the interior of the conical horn is separable into an attenuation region and a transmission region, whose mutual boundary is not sharply defined. Buchholz [36] has taken as boundary the surface of a sphere of radius R, where $(\omega/v)R = n + \frac{1}{2}$.

The symmetrical cases where $m = 0$, the E_0 and H_0 waves, have been treated in detail by Buchholz. The H_1 wave, $m = 1$, is perhaps the most useful when the horn is used as a radiator. Curves giving the lowest value of n determined by the boundary conditions for

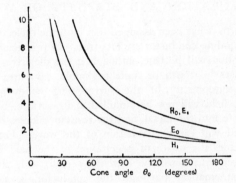

FIG. 16.—Values of n determining the propagation function $H_{n+\frac{1}{2}}^{(2)}(\omega r/v)$ in a conical horn. For wave E_0, $P_n(\cos \frac{1}{2}\theta_0) = 0$; H_0, E_1, $(d/d\theta_0)P_n(\cos \frac{1}{2}\theta_0) = 0$; H_1, $(d/d\theta_0)P_n^1(\cos \frac{1}{2}\theta_0) = 0$.

E_0, E_1, H_0 and H_1 waves are shown in Figure 16. The curves for E_1 and H_0 coincide, since

$$P_n^1 (\cos \theta) = - (d/d\theta)P_n(\cos \theta).$$

These waves bear a close resemblance to the corresponding types in a circular guide, and their wave patterns are essentially those of Figure 7 distorted to fit a conical surface.

Further cases of surfaces composed by polar coordinate surfaces have been treated by Sonoda [37], Buchholz [36] and Barrow, Chu and Jansen [59].

CHAPTER III

ATTENUATION AND STABILITY OF WAVES

HITHERTO it has been assumed that both the dielectric and the bounding conductor are loss-free. In practice neither assumption will be true, although if the dielectric be air the losses in it will be quite negligible. Because of the finite conductivity of the surrounding conductor the electric field will not be annulled at its surface, but will penetrate into the metal, and the resistance losses thereby incurred will cause attenuation of the wave. For good conductors the depth of penetration of the field at very high frequencies will be extremely small, and, although for mathematical purposes the conductor is assumed infinitely thick, in practice it can be quite thin-walled.

The attenuation caused by conductor and dielectric losses was first studied for circular tubes by Barrow [18] and in the papers from the Bell Laboratories [19], [20]. Their results have been extended and the methods modified by Clavier [23], Chu and Barrow [15], Rytov [10] and others. The straightforward method of approach is to include in Maxwell's equations the term involving the conductivity σ and proceed as before, this time applying boundary conditions appropriate to the surface of separation between two materials characterized by ε, μ, σ for the dielectric and ε_1, μ_1, σ_1 for the metal. This method is tedious, and the following simpler procedure is available, in which the two sources of loss are treated separately.

ATTENUATION DUE TO CONDUCTOR RESISTANCE

Let a semi-infinite perfectly conducting mass have as surface the plane $z = 0$ and let n be a unit vector normal to $z = 0$ and directed away from the metal. An electromagnetic field whose magnetic component at the surface is H_S induces a surface current of density K in the metal given by

$$n \times H_S = \frac{4\pi}{c} K, \quad . \quad . \quad . \quad (3.1)$$

and boundary conditions require that H_S be tangential to the surface.

When the metal has finite conductivity σ_1, the surface current is replaced by a volume distribution of density j. The theory of skin effect † gives

$$j = j_0 e^{-z/d} \cos(\omega t - z/d), \quad . \quad . \quad (3.2)$$

where $d = c/(2\pi\sigma_1\mu_1\omega)^{\frac{1}{2}}$, σ_1 being in e.s.u. If this volume distribution is to be equivalent to the surface current density of magnitude K in the perfectly conducting case, then

$$K = \int_0^\infty j\,dz = \frac{j_0 d}{\sqrt{2}} \cos(\omega t - \pi/4). \quad . \quad (3.3)$$

The mean power dissipated in heat per unit area of surface is then

$$\bar{P}_1 = \frac{\omega}{2\pi\sigma_1} \int_{t=0}^{t=2\pi/\omega} \int_{z=0}^{z=\infty} j^2\,dt\,dz = \frac{j_0^2 d}{4\sigma_1},$$

which becomes, using (3.1) and (3.3),

$$\bar{P}_1 = \frac{c}{16\pi}\left(\frac{\mu_1 f}{\sigma_1}\right)^{\frac{1}{2}} H_S \cdot H_S^*. \quad . \quad (3.4)$$

H^*, the complex conjugate of H, is introduced since complex quantities are involved, and the product $H_S \cdot H_S^*$ gives the square of the amplitude of H_S.

† Jeans, *Electricity and Magnetism*, Cambridge University Press, 1920 (p. 477).

This theory can be assumed to apply to a curved surface, provided the depth of penetration of the field into the metal is small compared with the radii of curvature of the surface. At very high frequencies this is true except in the immediate neighbourhood of a sharp corner, in which case the area concerned is so small as to produce a negligible error. It may also be postulated that, to a first approximation, the expressions for the field components will be unchanged from those of the loss-free case. Then the power loss $\bar{P}$ per unit length of tube is the integral of $\bar{P}_1$ around the periphery of a cross-section.

The average rate of energy flow in the axial direction is determined by the real part of the z-component of the complex Poynting vector as

$$\bar{W} = \frac{c}{4\pi} \int_A \overline{[Re(E) \times Re(H)]_z} \, dA$$

$$= \frac{c}{8\pi} Re \int_A (E \times H^*)_z \, dA. \qquad . \qquad (3.5)$$

Integration extends over the area A of a cross-section of the tube. The resistance loss occurs at the expense of the energy flow down the tube, so that $\bar{P}$ is equal to the rate of decrease of $\bar{W}$ along the axis. If the exponential attenuation factor which is thus introduced into all the field components be $\exp(-\alpha z)$, α can now be calculated, for

$$\bar{P} = -\frac{d\bar{W}}{dz} = -2\alpha\bar{W}.$$

Hence
$$\alpha = \frac{\bar{P}}{2\bar{W}}. \qquad . \qquad . \qquad . \qquad . \qquad (3.6)$$

ATTENUATION IN RECTANGULAR TUBES

From the expressions given in (1.16) and (1.18) for the field components of E and H waves in a rectangular wave guide the attenuation constants for these waves are determined.

E Waves. The mean power dissipated per unit length is

$$\bar{P} = \frac{c}{16\pi}\left(\frac{\mu_1 f}{\sigma_1}\right)^{\frac{1}{2}}\left[2\int_0^b (H_y H_y^*)_{x=0} dy + 2\int_0^a (H_x H_x^*)_{y=0} dx\right]$$

$$= \frac{c}{16\pi}\left(\frac{\mu_1 f}{\sigma_1}\right)^{\frac{1}{2}}\left(\frac{\pi\omega\varepsilon}{k^2 c}\right)^2\left(\frac{m^2 b}{a^2} + \frac{n^2 a}{b^2}\right).$$

For the mean energy flow through any cross-section

$$\bar{W} = \frac{c}{8\pi}\int_0^a\int_0^b (E_x H_y^* - E_y H_x^*) dx\, dy$$

$$= \frac{\omega\varepsilon a b\beta}{32\pi k^2}.$$

The attenuation constant derived from these values by means of (3.6) is

$$\alpha = \frac{1}{b}\left(\frac{\varepsilon\mu_1 f}{\mu\sigma_1}\right)^{\frac{1}{2}}\frac{\left(\dfrac{b}{a}\right)^3 m^2 + n^2}{\left(\dfrac{b}{a}\right)^2 m^2 + n^2}\frac{1}{\{1 - (f_0/f)^2\}^{\frac{1}{2}}}, \qquad (3.7)$$

f_0 being the appropriate critical frequency for the wave concerned.

H Waves. In this case $\bar{P}$ and $\bar{W}$ are given by

$$\bar{P} = \frac{c}{16\pi}\left(\frac{\mu_1 f}{\sigma_1}\right)^{\frac{1}{2}}\left[2\int_0^b (H_y H_y^* + H_z H_z^*)_{x=0} dy\right.$$
$$\left. + 2\int_0^a (H_x H_x^* + H_z H_z^*)_{y=0} dx\right]$$

$$= \frac{c}{16\pi}\left(\frac{\mu_1 f}{\sigma_1}\right)^{\frac{1}{2}}\left[\frac{\pi^2\beta^2}{k^4}\left(\frac{m^2}{a} + \frac{n^2}{b}\right) + a + b\right],$$

$$\bar{W} = \frac{c}{8\pi}\int_0^a\int_0^b (E_x H_y^* - E_y H_x^*) dx\, dy$$

$$= \frac{\omega\mu a b\beta}{32\pi k^2}.$$

Hence

$$\alpha = \frac{1}{b}\left(\frac{\varepsilon\mu_1 f}{\mu\sigma_1}\right)^{\frac{1}{2}}\left[\frac{\dfrac{b}{a}\left(\dfrac{b}{a}m^2+n^2\right)}{\left(\dfrac{b}{a}\right)^2 m^2+n^2}\{1-(f_0/f)^2\}+\left(1+\frac{b}{a}\right)\left(\frac{f_0}{f}\right)^2\right]$$

$$\times \frac{1}{\{1-(f_0/f)^2\}^{\frac{1}{2}}}. \qquad (3.8)$$

if $m \neq 0$ and $n \neq 0$.

Since these values include factors of $\frac{1}{2}$ obtained from the integration of $\cos^2 m\pi x/a$ and $\cos^2 n\pi y/b$ they will not hold for m or n zero. For the H_{m0} wave the appropriate expression for α is

$$\alpha = \frac{1}{b}\left(\frac{\varepsilon\mu_1 f}{\mu\sigma_1}\right)^{\frac{1}{2}}\left[\frac{1}{2}+\frac{b}{a}\left(\frac{f_0}{f}\right)^2\right]\frac{1}{\{1-(f_0/f)^2\}^{\frac{1}{2}}}. \quad (3.9)$$

For an H_{0n} wave a and b in (3.9) are interchanged.

The form of these expressions makes it difficult to estimate the effect of variations in frequency and dimensions. For a given frequency the attenuation constant can always be decreased by increasing the dimensions of the tube, but in practice this process is obviously limited, and the possibility of the appearance of unwanted higher-order waves must be considered. Comparing tubes of varying cross-section, but with constant perimeter, and hence constant mass of metal, we obtain a minimum attenuation for a given frequency when $\partial\alpha/\partial a - \partial\alpha/\partial b = 0$. The optimum ratio of a/b thus found varies with frequency, and the attenuation has an absolute minimum when in addition the frequency is such that $\partial\alpha/\partial f = 0$. Solution of these equations for the H_{10} wave gives the optimum value of a/b as 0·85 at an excitation wavelength of 0·14 × perimeter, but Figure 17 shows that those values are not critical. However, these optimum conditions permit the simultaneous existence of other wave types, and it is

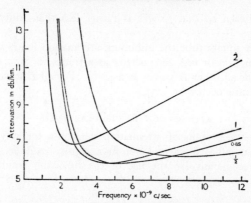

FIG. 17.—H_{10} wave in rectangular air-filled copper tube of perimeter 40 cm. for different a/b ratios.
($\sigma_1 = 54 \times 10^{16}$ e.s.u.)

usually more important to ensure that only one type can be propagated than to have minimum attenuation. The attenuation for the H_{10} wave is shown in Figure 18 for the

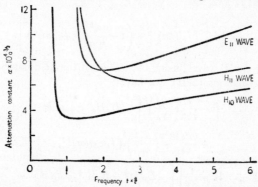

FIG. 18.—Attenuation in an air-filled copper guide with $a/b = 2$. Multiply ordinates by $86 \cdot 9 \times a^{-3/2}$ to give db./km.

usual ratio of sides $a/b = 2$, along with that for H_{11} and E_{11} waves. The H_{10} minimum occurs at a frequency of $(1 + \sqrt{2})f_0$, but to avoid higher modes the guide dimensions are chosen so that $f \times a/c$ is rather less than unity, i.e. $f < 2f_0$.

In a square tube the minimum attenuation for H waves in which m or n is zero occurs at a frequency of $2 \cdot 96 \, f_0$, and for all other H waves at $2 \cdot 41 \, f_0$. For all E waves the minimum occurs at $\sqrt{3}f_0$.

ATTENUATION IN CIRCULAR TUBES

The derivation of attenuation constants for waves in circular tubes is carried out in a similar manner. The integrations involve the use of the following recurrence formulae :

$$J_n{}'(x) = J_{n-1}(x) - \frac{n}{x} J_n(x) \quad . \quad . \quad . \quad (3.10)$$

$$J_n{}'(x) = -J_{n+1}(x) + \frac{n}{x} J_n(x), \quad . \quad . \quad (3.11)$$

and the Lommel integral

$$\int_0^a x\{J_n(kx)\}^2 dx$$

$$= \tfrac{1}{2}a^2\left[\{J_n{}'(ka)\}^2 + \left(1 - \frac{n^2}{k^2 a^2}\right)\{J_n(ka)\}^2 \right]. \quad (3.12)$$

For the E waves, using the values of the field components in equations (2.24), we have

$$\bar{P} = \frac{c}{16\pi}\left(\frac{\mu_1 f}{\sigma_1}\right)^{\frac{1}{2}} \int_0^{2\pi} (H_\phi H_\phi{}^*)_{\rho=a} a \, d\phi$$

$$= \frac{\omega^2 \varepsilon^2 k^2 a}{16c}\left(\frac{\mu_1 f}{\sigma_1}\right)^{\frac{1}{2}}\{J_{n-1}(ka)\}^2,$$

and $\quad \bar{W} = \frac{c}{8\pi}\iint_A (E_\rho H_\phi{}^* - E_\phi H_\rho{}^*)\rho \, d\rho \, d\phi$

$$= \frac{\beta\omega\varepsilon k^2 a^2}{16}\{J_{n-1}(ka)\}^2.$$

Hence $\quad \alpha = \frac{\bar{P}}{2\bar{W}} = \frac{1}{2a}\left(\frac{\varepsilon\mu_1 f}{\mu\sigma_1}\right)^{\frac{1}{2}}\frac{1}{\{1 - (f_0/f)^2\}^{\frac{1}{2}}}. \quad . \quad . \quad (3.13)$

For H waves it can be shown similarly that

$$\bar{P} = \frac{c}{16\pi}\left(\frac{\mu_1 f}{\sigma_1}\right)^{\frac{1}{2}}\int_0^{2\pi}(H_\phi H_\phi{}^* + H_z H_z{}^*)_{\rho=a}a\,d\phi$$

$$= \frac{ck^4a}{16}\left(\frac{\mu_1 f}{\sigma_1}\right)^{\frac{1}{2}}\left(\frac{n^2\beta^2}{k^4a^2} + 1\right)\{J_n(ka)\}^2,$$

$$\bar{W} = \frac{c}{8\pi}\iint_A(E_\rho H_\phi{}^* - E_\phi H_\rho{}^*)\rho\,d\rho\,d\phi$$

$$= \frac{\beta\omega\mu k^2 a^2}{16}\left(1 - \frac{n^2}{k^2a^2}\right)\{J_n(ka)\}^2,$$

and

$$\alpha = \frac{1}{2a}\left(\frac{\varepsilon\mu_1 f}{\mu\sigma_1}\right)^{\frac{1}{2}}\left[\left(\frac{f_0}{f}\right)^2 + \frac{n^2}{k^2a^2 - n^2}\right]\frac{1}{\{1 - (f_0/f)^2\}^{\frac{1}{2}}}. \quad (3.14)$$

Both (3.13) and (3.14) hold for zero order waves, although, due to the absence of the sine and cosine factors, the expressions for $\bar{P}$ and $\bar{W}$ must in that case be multiplied by a factor of 2.

Curves are given in Figure 19 of the variation with

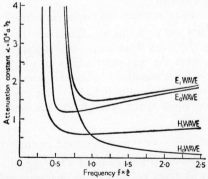

FIG. 19.—Attenuation in a circular air-filled copper tube. Multiply ordinates by $86\cdot9 \times a^{-3/2}$ to give db./km.

frequency of the attenuation constant for E_0, E_1, H_0 and H_1 waves in a tube of given diameter. Starting at an infinite value at the critical frequency, the attenuation decreases rapidly with increase of frequency, passes through a minimum and then rises steadily.

An important exception is the behaviour of the attenuation curves of the H_{0m} series of waves, which decrease continuously with increasing frequency, and in the limit approach zero. The following considerations make clearer the nature of this radical difference from all other wave types. The attenuation constant is proportional to the power losses in the tube for a given transmitted power. These losses depend on longitudinal and transverse currents induced in the walls of the tube, the former determined by the product $H_\phi H_\phi^*$ and the latter by $H_z H_z^*$. For a constant value of $\bar{W}$, the part due to $H_z H_z^*$ is proportional to $f^{-\frac{3}{2}}$ for large values of f; that due to $H_\phi H_\phi^*$ increases with frequency as $f^{\frac{1}{2}}$. The second term disappears if the transverse component of magnetic force is purely radial, i.e. for the H_{0m} waves, and the attenuation constant is then dependent only on a term which approaches zero with increasing frequency.

The frequency at which the minimum in the attenuation curve occurs is $\sqrt{3}f_0$ for all E waves. For H waves (excluding H_0) there is no simple expression; in the case of the H_1 wave the minimum occurs at $3 \cdot 15\ f_0$.

Formulae for attenuation coefficients of waves in elliptic tubes have been derived by Chu [33]. The expressions are complicated, and their evaluation involves graphical integration.

ATTENUATION DUE TO DIELECTRIC CONDUCTIVITY

Additional attenuation is caused when the tube encloses a dielectric of finite conductivity. A term involving this conductivity σ is then introduced into Maxwell's first equation, which becomes

$$\frac{\varepsilon}{c} \frac{\partial E}{\partial t} + \frac{4\pi\sigma}{c} E = \text{curl } H. \quad \cdot \quad \cdot \quad \cdot \quad (3.15)$$

Since this can be written

$$\frac{i\omega}{c}\left(\varepsilon - \frac{4\pi i\sigma}{\omega}\right)E = \text{curl } H,$$

the results of the previous work can be applied if ε is there replaced by $\varepsilon - 4\pi i\sigma/\omega$. In the tubes of constant cross-section which have been studied, the propagation constant γ for a perfect dielectric is determined by the relation

$$k^2 = \frac{\omega^2\varepsilon\mu}{c^2} + \gamma^2,$$

where the value of k depends on the shape of the cross-section. On replacing ε in this equation by $\varepsilon - 4\pi i\sigma/\omega$, we get,

$$\gamma^2 = (\alpha + i\beta)^2 = \alpha^2 - \beta^2 + 2i\alpha\beta$$

$$= k^2 - \frac{\omega^2\varepsilon\mu}{c^2} + \frac{4\pi i\omega\mu\sigma}{c^2}.$$

Then, assuming the conductivity to be small,

$$\beta \simeq \left[\frac{\omega^2}{v^2} - k^2\right]^{\frac{1}{2}} = \frac{\omega}{v}\{1 - (f_0/f)^2\}^{\frac{1}{2}}, \quad . \text{ (3.16)}$$

$$\alpha \simeq \frac{2\pi\sigma}{c}\left(\frac{\mu}{\varepsilon}\right)^{\frac{1}{2}}\frac{1}{\{1 - (f_0/f)^2\}^{\frac{1}{2}}}. \quad . \quad . \text{ (3.17)}$$

To a first approximation the presence of a small conductivity in the dielectric does not alter the phase constant and critical frequencies, but produces in the transmission region an attenuation constant given by (3.17). The form of the expression for α is the same for all uniform cross-sections and wave types, particular cases being determined by the appropriate value of f_0. At the critical frequency the attenuation constant is infinite, and decreases rapidly with increase of frequency to approach a limiting value of $(2\pi\sigma/c)(\mu/\varepsilon)^{\frac{1}{2}}$.

When both dielectric and conductor losses are present, the total attenuation constant is the sum of the two appropriate values of α.

PRACTICAL CONSIDERATIONS

The expressions already given for attenuation constants are the coefficients of the exponential propagation factor and are thus in nepers/cm. In engineering practice attenuations are usually expressed in decibels, given by ten times the common logarithm of the ratio of input power to output power. Since this power ratio is $\exp(2\alpha z)$, the attenuation per unit length is

$$N = 20\alpha \log_{10} e = 8\cdot686\alpha \text{ decibels/cm.}$$

For wave guides to be of practical use it must be shown that their attenuation constants are comparable with that of the conventional coaxial transmission line. From equations (2.31) it is found that the attenuation constant for conductor loss in a coaxial line with conductors of radii a and b ($a > b$) is

$$\alpha = \frac{1}{2a} \left(\frac{\varepsilon \mu_1 f}{\mu \sigma_1} \right)^{\frac{1}{2}} \frac{1 + a/b}{2 \log (a/b)}. \quad . \quad . \quad (3.18)$$

The ratio of a/b for which this is a minimum is $3\cdot6$. Figure 20 shows some attenuation constants for a circular wave guide and a coaxial line of optimum ratio, each having a diameter of 5 cm. and air dielectric. It is seen

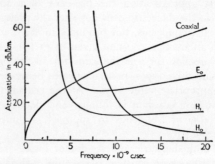

FIG. 20.—Relative attenuations in a circular wave guide and a coaxial line, each of 5 cm. diameter.

that if the frequency is sufficiently high—of the order of 1·2 times the critical frequency—the attenuation constants in the wave guide are less than in the coaxial line, notably so in the case of the H_0 wave. Thus, for frequencies corresponding to wavelengths of a few centimetres, a wave guide of reasonably small size can be a more efficient transmission line than one of the coaxial type. Its superiority is greater than the curves suggest, since the inner conductor of the coaxial line requires for its support some dielectric material. As the losses in the known solid dielectrics are high at these frequencies, even small insulating supports are likely to add considerable attenuation.

The theoretical attenuations for two of the standard copper rectangular guides, 2·84 × 1·34 inches and 0·9 × 0·4 inches, are respectively 0·019 db./m. at 10 cm. wavelength and 0·107 db./m. at 3 cm. wavelength for the H_{10} mode. In practice values are rather higher owing to surface effects which reduce conductivity.

The treatment of attenuation due to conductor loss used in this chapter is slightly unsatisfactory in its assumption that the phase constant remains unchanged from its value for the loss-free case. A perturbation method used by Oswald [71] shows that in the presence of attenuation the phase constant β is increased by a small amount $\delta\beta$ equal in magnitude to α. Since $\delta\beta/\beta$ is thus of the order of 10^{-4} the assumption made is quite justified.

EVANESCENT WAVES

In a perfectly conducting guide, when the frequency of oscillation is less than the critical frequency for a particular wave type the propagation constant γ becomes real; the wave is no longer freely propagated but decays exponentially as $e^{-\gamma z}$, γ being given by $\gamma^2 = k^2 - (\omega/v)^2$. Such a wave is known as an *evanescent wave*, and in it the mean

energy flow is zero.   For frequencies well below the critical
value γ becomes approximately equal to k, a constant
dependent only on tube dimensions.   This property is
made use of in the *piston attenuator*, where, by means of
a wave guide operating in an evanescent mode and containing two electrodes with variable separation, an attenuation is produced whose value in decibels is proportional
to the separation.   The E_{01} and H_{11} modes in a circular
tube are those especially used, and for a radius a cm. give
for γ respectively $2\cdot405/a$ and $1\cdot841/a$ nepers/cm., i.e.
$20\cdot9/a$ and $16\cdot0/a$ db./cm.   By analogy with the guide
wavelength $2\pi/\beta$ in the transmission case, which represents
the distance in which the phase changes by 2π, an *attenuation length* for the evanescent case can be defined as $2\pi/\gamma$,
giving the distance in which the wave is attenuated by
2π nepers ;   the phase remains constant.

The approximations made in deriving the formulae for
attenuation in the regions above and below a critical frequency do not hold in the neighbourhood of this frequency ;
they approach infinity and zero respectively.   For the
case of an H_{m0} wave in a rectangular guide Käch [74] has
derived a complete formula showing a smooth transition
from one to the other.

STABILITY OF WAVE TYPES TO IRREGULARITIES

As any tube used for wave transmission is likely to have
slight deviations from its nominal cross-section, it is
necessary to investigate whether or not the various wave
types are stable under such deviations.

For a circular tube a slight deformation may be assumed
to produce an elliptical cross-section of small eccentricity.
Wave propagation will then be in accordance with the
theory on elliptic cylinders in Chapter II. Using the
symbols introduced there, the distance between the foci
is $2g$ and the eccentricity of the confocal ellipses is $1/\cosh \xi$,
and hence the transition from the elliptical to the circular

case is the limit when $g \rightarrow 0$ and $\xi \rightarrow \infty$. The semi-major and semi-minor axes are $g \cosh \xi$ and $g \sinh \xi$, so that $g \cosh \xi \rightarrow g \sinh \xi \rightarrow \rho$, and η becomes the polar angle ϕ between the x-axis and the radius vector ρ. The limiting values of the Mathieu functions as the ellipse approaches a circle are (p_n and p_n' being constants)

$$\lim ce_n(\eta, q) = \cos n\phi, \quad \lim se_n(\eta, q) = \sin n\phi,$$
$$\lim ce_n(i\xi, q) = p_n J_n(k\rho), \quad \lim se_n(i\xi, q) = p_n' J_n(k\rho).$$

Application of these limits to the E_z components derived from the functions U, (2.38), for the elliptic cylinder gives

$$E_{cn} \text{ wave}: \quad E_z = k_c^2 ce_n(i\xi, q) \, ce_n(\eta, q) \, e^{-i\beta_c z}$$
$$\rightarrow p_n k^2 J_n(k\rho) \cos n\phi \, e^{-i\beta z}.$$

$$E_{sn} \text{ wave}: \quad E_z = k_s^2 se_n(i\xi, q) \, se_n(\eta, q) \, e^{-i\beta_s z}$$
$$\rightarrow p_n' k^2 J_n(k\rho) \sin n\phi \, e^{-i\beta z}.$$

For an E wave in a circular tube the general expression for E_z (by 2.15) is

$$E_z = (A \cos n\phi + B \sin n\phi) J_n(k\rho) \, e^{-i\beta z}, \qquad (3.19)$$

where A/B depends on the relation of the nodal planes of the wave to the $\phi = 0$ axis. If the coordinate system is chosen so that at the deformation the major axis of the ellipse lies along the $\phi = 0$ axis, then an E wave so orientated that E_z is dependent only on $\cos n\phi$ will become an E_{cn} wave —an even wave—in the deformed tube; one dependent only upon $\sin n\phi$ will become an odd wave, E_{sn}. The same correspondence holds for H waves. In general a wave will be so orientated as to include both sine and cosine terms, and can be regarded as composed of two distinct components travelling with the same phase velocity. In the deformed part of the tube an odd and an even wave will result. As the critical wavelengths of these two waves are different (see Figure 11) they will travel with different phase velocities and will separate. In consequence, waves in a circular tube tend to be unstable under slight cross-

5

sectional deformations. To this general conclusion there are two important exceptions. Firstly, if the deformation occurs along an axis of symmetry of the wave, i.e. if A or B of (3.19) is zero, the deformed wave will be either odd or even only, and there will be no splitting. Secondly, for waves of zero order, $n = 0$, there is no odd wave in an elliptic tube, thus again no separation can occur. Conclusions are that for slight deformations of the cross-section of a circular wave guide :

(1) E_0 and H_0 waves are stable,

(2) All other waves are unstable except to deformations along an axis of symmetry of the wave.

The derivation of these results is due to Brillouin [7] and Chu [33]. From the expressions derived by Chu for the attenuation of waves in elliptic tubes, it appears that the attenuation curve of the deformed H_0 wave loses its anomalous character, and assumes the normal form, having a minimum in the transmission region and eventually increasing steadily with frequency. This is due to a term proportional to $f^{\frac{1}{2}}$ which is absent only when the eccentricity is zero. By keeping the eccentricity sufficiently small the attenuation minimum can be made to occur at a frequency as far above the critical frequency as desired. It has also been shown that, of the pair of waves formed by deformation of an E_1 or H_1 wave, one component wave has a higher attenuation than the other and may become negligible after travelling some distance.

In a rectangular tube slight change in the dimensions does not cause instability, for it only alters slightly the propagation constants and does not make possible any new wave types. However, instability is possible if two waves are superposed which belong to distinct transmission modes having the same critical frequency. For example, in a square tube an H_{01} and an H_{10} wave travel with the same velocity and can be superposed to form a single resultant which is transmitted without change of form. When the tube is deformed so as to be slightly oblong the two components assume different velocities respectively greater and less than the original velocity, and the compound wave will suffer continuous change of pattern as it proceeds.

THE EFFECT OF BENDS AND DISCONTINUITIES

The study of the effect of bends in a wave guide is of importance for practical applications. A rectangular guide of sides a and b, bent into an arc of a circle as in Figure 21, has a surface given in cylindrical polars by $\rho = \rho_1$, ρ_2, $z = 0$, b and $\rho_2 - \rho_1 = a$. The equation to be solved for the function U is the same as that for circular cylindrical

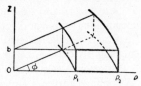

FIG. 21.—Coordinate system for a curved rectangular guide.

guides (2.14), but a solution must be chosen which will give a travelling wave in the ϕ-direction and stationary waves in the ρ- and z-directions. For free propagation with phase constant β inside a perfect conductor the appropriate function is

$$U = [AJ_\beta(k\rho) + BY_\beta(k\rho)](C \cos pz + D \sin pz)\, e^{-i\beta\phi},$$

where p and β are as yet undetermined, and $k^2 = (\omega/v)^2 - p^2$. Solving for the field components by equations (2.12), and applying the boundary conditions that E_ρ, E_ϕ are zero at $z = 0, b$, E_z zero at $\rho = \rho_1, \rho_2$, the expression for U becomes

$$U = [Y_\beta(k\rho_1)J_\beta(k\rho) - J_\beta(k\rho_1)Y_\beta(k\rho)] \cos \frac{n\pi z}{b}\, e^{-i\beta\phi}, \quad (3.20)$$

where $\qquad k^2 = (\omega/v)^2 - (n\pi/b)^2, \qquad n = 0, 1, 2, \ldots\ ,$

and β is determined by the relation

$$Y_\beta(k\rho_1)J_\beta(k\rho_2) - J_\beta(k\rho_1)Y_\beta(k\rho_2) = 0\ . \quad (3.21)$$

For the solution (2.13) the expression for V is

$$V = [Y_{\beta}'(k\rho_1)J_{\beta}(k\rho) - J_{\beta}'(k\rho_1)Y_{\beta}(k\rho)] \sin\frac{n\pi z}{b} e^{-i\beta\phi}, \quad . \; (3.22)$$

with $\qquad k^2 = (\omega/v)^2 - (n\pi/b)^2, \qquad n = 1,2,3, \ldots,$

and β is determined by

$$Y_{\beta}'(k\rho_1)J_{\beta}'(k\rho_2) - J_{\beta}'(k\rho_1)Y_{\beta}'(k\rho_2) = 0. \quad . \; (3.23)$$

The solutions obtained from (3.20) and (3.22) have H_z and E_z zero respectively, and hence are not true E and H waves, but correspond to what have been called longitudinal-section waves in a straight rectangular guide.

Buchholz [38] has obtained expansions in series for values of β satisfying (3.21) and (3.23), and has shown that, when ρ_1, ρ_2 become large compared with a and b, the propagation approximates to that of longitudinal-section waves in a straight tube. Thus slightly curved rectangular tubes will transmit with little distortion waves in which the magnetic or electric vector is confined to the ρ,ϕ-plane. Any E or H wave can be regarded as a combination of two such component waves travelling with equal phase velocities in a straight tube; each component will be transmitted undistorted round a bend, but in the bend the two have different phase velocities. After negotiating the bend these components will not combine into the original wave, but will form a mixed wave. An exception is a wave determined by (3.21) with $n = 0$, when the field components E_ρ, E_ϕ, and H_z are zero. This is a longitudinal-section wave, but, since E_ϕ is zero, it is also a true H wave, corresponding to an H_{m0} wave in a straight rectangular guide. This case has been studied in detail by Jouguet [79]. In particular, for the H_{10} wave in a guide capable of supporting only this mode, the following conditions hold. The propagation constants in straight and curved guides differ only by a term of the second order in a/ρ_1. To this order of approximation a wave passing from a straight guide into a curved one suffers no change in amplitude or phase. A series of evanescent modes of even order, H_{20}, $H_{40}, \ldots$, are set up in both directions at the junction, but these decay rapidly with distance and cause no loss of energy. Such a bend is known as an *H bend*, the plane of the bend being parallel to the plane of the magnetic field. A bend in the other plane is an *E bend*.

An exact study of the effect of bends in a circular guide would involve the use of toroidal coordinates, but solutions of the vector wave equation in this system are not known. An analysis by Jouguet [79], using a perturbation method valid for a large radius of curvature, shows that the problem is very complex, except in the case of the E_0 wave. An E_0 wave in a straight guide is transformed into an E_0 wave in the curved guide with the addition of parasitic E_1 and H_1 waves of small amplitude. The propagation constant is, to the second order, independent of curvature.

The work of the last two sections gives only qualitative answers to the problems considered. Much will depend on the precise form and sharpness of the distortions and bends introduced, and theory will have to be supplemented by experimental observations. Any abrupt change of dimensions or shape of a wave guide will result in the formation of new waves regardless of the stability or instability of the wave originally present. These will be dependent on the nature of the change, their amplitudes being such as will satisfy boundary conditions at the surfaces of discontinuity, and determinable from Fourier or Fourier-Bessel expansions. Of the modes produced, only those whose phase constants are real will be propagated ; types of higher order will have an exponential propagation factor, and suffer rapid attenuation.

The properties of junctions between two rectangular guides of different dimensions are treated briefly in Chapter VII.

POWER HANDLING CAPACITY

The power which can be transmitted down a uniform wave guide is normally limited by breakdown in the dielectric. If the power is expressed in terms of the maximum value of the electric field, then the power transmitted for an assigned maximum field can be calculated. In air at atmospheric pressure the electric strength at high frequencies is nearly the same as the d.c. value of 30 kV./cm., or 100 e.s.u./cm.

For an H_{10} wave in an air-filled rectangular guide the maximum field is the value of E_y at $x = \frac{1}{2}a$, and hence, from the expression for energy flow,

$$\bar{W} = (E_{max.})^2 \frac{cab}{16\pi}\{1 - (f_0/f)^2\}^{\frac{1}{2}} \text{ erg/sec.} \quad . \quad (3.24)$$

The limiting power in a 0·9 × 0·4 inch wave guide operated at a wavelength $\lambda = 4a/3$, that is at a frequency $f = 3f_0/2$, is thus $\bar{W} = 1·05 \times 10^{13}$ erg/sec. $= 1·05$ MW.

For an E wave the maximum field may be given by either the longitudinal or a transverse component. In a circular guide transmitting an E_{01} wave the radial component, which has a maximum at a radius of 0·77a, is the limiting one for frequencies well removed from the critical frequency. At frequencies less than about $2f_0$ the field along the axis predominates, and then the power transmitted is given by

$$\bar{W} = 0·23(E_{max.})^2 \frac{a^4 f^2}{c}\{1 - (f_0/f)^2\}^{\frac{1}{2}} \text{ erg/sec.} \quad . \quad (3.25)$$

CHAPTER IV

FURTHER WAVE PROPERTIES

WAVE IMPEDANCE

In transmission line theory a fundamental parameter is the characteristic impedance, which is defined as the ratio of voltage to current at any point in an infinite line. For wave guide transmission, characteristic impedances have been determined by some authors from voltages and currents derived by integration of the field components. The definitions of these are somewhat arbitrary, and a more satisfactory procedure is due to Schelkunoff [65], who has extended the impedance concept so that *wave impedances* are defined as ratios of field components. For waves referred to an orthogonal coordinate system, u_1, u_2, u_3, the wave impedance Z_3 in the direction of propagation u_3 is given by

$$Z_3 = \frac{E_1}{H_2} = -\frac{E_2}{H_1}. \quad . \quad . \quad (4.1)$$

Hence, from equations (2.12) and (2.13), the impedance for E waves in a uniform tube of any section is

$$Z_3 = \left(\frac{\mu}{\varepsilon}\right)^{\frac{1}{2}} \{1 - (f_0/f)^2\}^{\frac{1}{2}} = \left(\frac{\mu}{\varepsilon}\right)^{\frac{1}{2}} \frac{\lambda}{\lambda_t}, \quad . \quad (4.2)$$

and for H waves is

$$Z_3 = \left(\frac{\mu}{\varepsilon}\right)^{\frac{1}{2}} \frac{1}{\{1 - (f_0/f)^2\}^{\frac{1}{2}}} = \left(\frac{\mu}{\varepsilon}\right)^{\frac{1}{2}} \frac{\lambda_t}{\lambda} \quad . \quad (4.3)$$

The appropriate value of f_0 must be substituted for the particular cross-section of tube and wave type considered.

For frequencies well above the critical values both impedances approach the value $(\mu/\varepsilon)^{\frac{1}{2}}$. Wave impedances for E waves vary from zero at the critical frequency up to this value; for H waves the range is from infinity down to $(\mu/\varepsilon)^{\frac{1}{2}}$. The wave impedance is also $(\mu/\varepsilon)^{\frac{1}{2}}$ for plane transverse waves of all frequencies in an unlimited medium, and is known as the *intrinsic impedance* of the medium. When ε and μ have their free-space values, which in practical units are respectively $(1/36\pi) \times 10^{-9}$ farad/metre and $4\pi \times 10^{-7}$ henry/metre, the value of $(\mu/\varepsilon)^{\frac{1}{2}}$ is 120π or 377 ohms—the intrinsic impedance of free space.

The wave impedance has properties similar to that of characteristic impedance in transmission lines. For instance, all the energy travelling along a wave guide will be absorbed without reflexion by a resistive film having a surface resistivity equal to the appropriate value of Z_z, i.e. in an air-filled guide $120\pi \lambda/\lambda_t$ ohms/cm.^{2} for an E wave, and $120\pi \lambda_t/\lambda$ ohms/cm.^{2} for an H wave. For a transverse wave in a coaxial line, the wave impedance, from (2.31), is $(\mu/\varepsilon)^{\frac{1}{2}}$. If a film of this resistivity be placed across the end of the line, the resistance thus applied between outer and inner conductors of radii a and b is

$$\int_b^a \left(\frac{\mu}{\varepsilon}\right)^{\frac{1}{2}} \frac{dr}{2\pi r} = 60 \log \frac{a}{b} \quad \text{ohms,}$$

which is the expression for the characteristic impedance of a coaxial line with air dielectric.

For an H_{10} wave in a rectangular guide a voltage and current can be derived which are formally equivalent to those of a two-conductor transmission line. If the field equations for the wave are put in the form

$$E_y = E_0 \sin \frac{\pi x}{a}, \qquad H_x = H_0 \sin \frac{\pi x}{a},$$

then the expression for the mean energy flow can be written as

$$\bar{W} = \frac{c}{16\pi} ab\, E_0 H_0 \quad = \frac{1}{2} \frac{b E_0}{\sqrt{2}} \frac{a K_0}{\sqrt{2}},$$

where K_0 is the induced surface current density given by
(3.1). Taking $bE_0/\sqrt{2}$ as defining an equivalent potential
difference V between the horizontal walls and $aK_0/\sqrt{2}$ as
a current I flowing along these walls, we obtain the usual
power equation

$$\bar{W} = \tfrac{1}{2}VI.$$

For this a characteristic impedance can be defined as

$$Z_0 \text{ (ohms)} = 10^{-9}c^2\, V/I$$

$$= 120\pi\frac{b}{a}\frac{E_0}{H_0} = \frac{b}{a}Z_z \quad . \quad . \quad (4.4)$$

Such currents and voltages are not readily measurable,
however, in wave guides, and the quantities which are
most conveniently measured are the transmitted power and
the standing wave ratio of the field. The latter can be
used to derive the normal impedance relationships of
two-conductor transmission lines. If a guide is terminated
by an impedance having a reflection factor $\rho = |\rho|\, e^{i\phi}$,
and a wave of unit amplitude is incident on this termination,
then the amplitude and phase of the reflected wave at
a point distant l from the termination are given relative
to the incident wave at that point by $\rho e^{-2i\beta l}$, or

$$|\rho|\exp i(\phi - 2\beta l).$$

Minimum and maximum values of the combination are
$1 - |\rho|$ and $1 + |\rho|$. If the ratio of these two defines
the standing wave ratio S—a measurable quantity—then
$|\rho|$ is determined by

$$|\rho| = \frac{1 - S}{1 + S}.$$

If l is taken as the measured distance of the maximum near-
est to the termination, then $\phi - 2\beta l = 0$, that is $\phi = 4\pi l/\lambda_t$.
Hence ρ is determined experimentally in amplitude and
phase. Now if Z_z and Z_t are the wave impedances of the
guide and its termination, the reflection factor will be given,
just as in ordinary transmission line theory, by

$$\rho = (Z_t - Z_z)/(Z_t + Z_z).$$

Whence $Z_t/Z_z = (1 + \rho)/(1 - \rho)$, and this relation can be written as Z_t, the normalized wave impedance of the termination. Thus discontinuities of all types can be expressed in terms of impedances which follow the well-known relationships of transmission line theory, and allow equivalent circuits to be derived. They must be used with understanding, however. Since the basis is electric and magnetic fields rather than the more tangible concepts of voltage and current, it is not immediately obvious whether a particular discontinuity is to be regarded as a parallel or a series impedance. This can be shown to depend on the type of scattering experienced by the wave at the discontinuity. *Symmetrical scattering*, in which equal reflected waves are set up in both directions with their electric fields in phase, and their magnetic fields in antiphase, corresponds to a parallel impedance, and is shown by a thin metal obstacle of any shape placed with its plane in the cross-section of the guide. In *anti-symmetrical* scattering the reflected electric fields are in antiphase and the magnetic fields in phase, the case of a series impedance. More complex cases where the scattering is unsymmetrical lead to equivalent circuits containing both series and parallel elements. The above principles are expounded in much more detail by Slater [69] and Huxley [72]; some applications will be found in Chapter VII.

For a wave guide of varying cross-section the wave impedance is, in general, complex. Thus, from (2.45), the wave impedance for an H_{n0} wave in a sectoral horn is

$$Z_\rho = -\frac{E_z}{H_\phi} = -i\left(\frac{\mu}{\varepsilon}\right)^{\frac{1}{2}} \frac{H^{(2)}_{n\pi/\phi_0}(\omega\rho/v)}{H^{(2)'}_{n\pi/\phi_0}(\omega\rho/v)}.$$

Of this the real and imaginary parts are, in terms of α and β as defined on p. 38,

$$R_\rho = \left(\frac{\mu}{\varepsilon}\right)^{\frac{1}{2}} \frac{\omega}{v} \frac{\beta}{\alpha^2 + \beta^2}, \qquad X_\rho = \left(\frac{\mu}{\varepsilon}\right)^{\frac{1}{2}} \frac{\omega}{v} \frac{\alpha}{\alpha^2 + \beta^2}.$$

In the attenuation region the resistive part of the wave impedance is small compared with the reactive part; in the transmission region the resistive part predominates. As the length of the horn is increased R_ρ approaches $(\mu/\varepsilon)^{\frac{1}{2}}$, while X_ρ approaches zero.

For E waves in a conical horn the wave impedance is

$$Z_r = i\left(\frac{\mu}{\varepsilon}\right)^{\frac{1}{2}} \frac{\dfrac{d}{dx}\{x^{\frac{1}{2}}H^{(2)}_{n+\frac{1}{2}}(x)\}}{x^{\frac{1}{2}}H^{(2)}_{n+\frac{1}{2}}(x)}, \quad . \quad . \quad . \quad (4.5)$$

where $x = \omega r/v$. This impedance has real and imaginary parts varying with r, and application of the asymptotic expression (2.43) for the Hankel function shows that it approaches a real value of $(\mu/\varepsilon)^{\frac{1}{2}}$ for large values of r. The wave impedance for H waves has similar properties.

At short wavelengths dielectric measurements are usually made on parallel wires or coaxial lines. For the centimetre and decimetre range of wavelength these can be replaced by the wave guide, which has the advantages that dimensions do not need to be small in comparison with the wavelength, and that dielectric specimens to fit the tube are easily made. Most of the methods developed for the other systems are adaptable to the wave guide, and the wave impedance is useful in deriving formulae. The methods used depend on measurement of the modification, by the insertion of dielectric material, of the standing wave pattern in a guide [11, 86, 91], or of the resonance properties of a hollow cavity [89].

OPTICAL PROPERTIES OF WAVE GUIDES

So far there has been only mathematical reasoning to explain the cut-off characteristic of wave guides. Physical reasoning gives no *a priori* explanation, but it is possible to express the mathematical results in a form which provides quite a satisfactory physical picture based on simple laws of geometrical optics. This method was first expounded by Brillouin [4] in 1936, and later extended by Page and Adams [6].

A plane polarized wave moving with velocity u in the direction represented by a unit vector n is expressed, in terms of its electric vector, by

$$E = E_0 \exp i\omega\left(t - \frac{r \cdot n}{u}\right), \quad \cdot \quad \cdot \quad \cdot \quad (4.6)$$

and, since the wave is plane, $n \cdot E_0 = 0$.

Consider the propagation of a wave in the z-direction in the simple wave guide of Figure 22, which is formed by

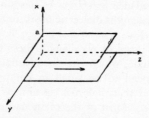

FIG. 22.—Parallel plane wave guide.

the two infinite parallel conducting planes $x = 0$ and $x = a$. Expressions for the wave can be deduced from equation (2.11) by regarding the problem as two-dimensional, independent of the y-coordinate. For the E_n wave the magnetic vector is in the direction of y, and the electric field components are found to be

$$\left.\begin{aligned} E_z &= \sin\frac{n\pi x}{a}\, e^{i(\omega t - \beta z)} \\ E_x &= -\frac{i\beta a}{n\pi}\cos\frac{n\pi x}{a}\, e^{i(\omega t - \beta z)}, \end{aligned}\right\} \quad \cdot \quad \cdot \quad (4.7)$$

with $\beta = \{(\omega/v)^2 - (n\pi/a)^2\}^{\frac{1}{2}}$. If i, j, k are unit vectors along the axes, the field E of (4.7) can be expressed as

$$E = \left(-i\frac{i\beta a}{n\pi}\cos\frac{n\pi x}{a} + k\sin\frac{n\pi x}{a}\right)e^{i(\omega t - \beta z)},$$

which becomes, on replacing sine and cosine by their complex exponential forms,

$$E = -\frac{i}{2}\left[\left(i\frac{\beta a}{n\pi} + k\right)e^{i(\omega t - \beta z + n\pi x/a)}\right.$$
$$\left. + \left(i\frac{\beta a}{n\pi} - k\right)e^{i(\omega t - \beta z - n\pi x/a)}\right]. \quad . \quad . \quad (4.8)$$

This is the sum of two waves travelling in directions given by

$$n = \frac{\pm n\pi/a, 0, \beta}{\{(n\pi/a)^2 + \beta^2\}^{\frac{1}{2}}} = \frac{\pm n\pi/a, 0, \beta}{\omega/v}, \quad . \quad (4.9)$$

and they are plane polarized, since

$$n \cdot E_0 = -\frac{i}{2}n \cdot \left(i\frac{\beta a}{n\pi} \mp k\right) = 0.$$

The directions of propagation are in the zx-plane, and make with the z-axis an angle C given by

$$\cos C = \beta v/\omega = \{1 - (f_0/f)^2\}^{\frac{1}{2}} = \lambda/\lambda_t. \quad . \quad . \quad (4.10)$$

The velocity of propagation u is, by (4.6),

$$u = \frac{\omega}{\{\beta^2 + (n\pi/a)^2\}^{\frac{1}{2}}} = v. \quad . \quad . \quad (4.11)$$

Thus an E wave propagated between two parallel plates is equivalent to the interference pattern of two plane polarized waves travelling with the normal velocity of light in the unbounded medium and reflected back and forth between the plates in a zigzag path. The angle of incidence of these *elementary waves* is dependent upon the ratio f/f_0.

At the critical frequency $f = f_0$, $C = 90°$, and the waves are reflected normally between the two walls without progressing. For values of f just greater than f_0, C is slightly less than $90°$, and slow progression takes place; with further increase of frequency C decreases steadily. The path of the elementary waves is shown in Figure 23

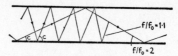

FIG. 23.—Path of the elementary waves between two conducting planes.

for $f/f_0 = 1\cdot1$ and $f/f_0 = 2$. In terms of C the phase velocity v' of the original wave is

$$v' = \frac{v}{\cos C}, \quad \cdots \quad (4.12)$$

which means that the interference fringes run parallel to the planes with a velocity $v/\cos C$, which becomes equal to the free wave velocity at grazing incidence, and infinite for normal incidence. The group velocity u' is given by

$$u' = \frac{v^2}{v'} = v \cos C. \quad \cdots \quad (4.13)$$

This is the effective forward velocity which would be calculated from the zigzag trajectory. An H wave can be compounded of two elementary waves, similar to these, but with different polarization.

For waves in a rectangular tube the expressions (1.16) and (1.18) are separable into four elementary waves with directions of propagation whose direction-cosines are

$$\frac{\pm m\pi/a, \pm n\pi/b, \beta}{\omega/v} \quad \cdots \quad (4.14)$$

Progressive reflexions occur at all four walls, and again the waves make an angle with the z-axis given by

$$\cos C = \{1 - (f_0/f)^2\}^{\frac{1}{2}} = \lambda/\lambda_t.$$

The process is thus essentially similar to the simple case first considered.

The wave types peculiar to circular wave guides can be synthesized from an infinite number of plane polarized waves travelling with normal velocity at an angle to the axis of the tube. An elementary wave travelling in the z, x-plane at an angle $- C$ to the z-axis has direction $\mathbf{n} = (- \sin C,\ 0,\ \cos C)$. If its magnetic vector H' lies along the y-axis, then its electric vector E' has direction $(\cos C,\ 0,\ \sin C)$. The components of E' along the co-ordinate axes are then

$$\left. \begin{aligned}
E_x' &= \cos C \exp i\omega\left(t - \frac{- x \sin C + z \cos C}{v} \right) \\
E_y' &= 0 \\
E_z' &= \sin C \exp i\omega\left(t - \frac{- x \sin C + z \cos C}{v} \right).
\end{aligned} \right\} \quad (4.15)$$

Let this set of axes be placed as shown in Figure 24(a) so that the x-axis makes an angle ψ with the radius vector to

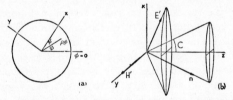

FIG. 24.—Cone of directions of the elementary waves in a circular guide.

the point (ρ, ϕ) inside the tube. The elementary wave associated with this position is given an amplitude of $A \cos n(\phi + \psi)\, d\psi$, and an infinite number of such waves is summed over the range of ψ from 0 to 2π. By the aid of Sommerfeld's integral,

$$J_n(x) = \frac{i^{-n}}{2\pi}\int_0^{2\pi} \exp\left(ix \cos \psi + in\, \psi\right) d\psi, \quad (4.16)$$

the z-component of the resultant electric field is evaluated
as

$$E_z = A \int_0^{2\pi} E_z' \cos n(\phi + \psi) \, d\psi$$

$$= A \sin C \int_0^{2\pi} \exp i\omega \left(t - \frac{-\rho \cos \psi \sin C + z \cos C}{v} \right)$$
$$\times \cos n(\phi + \psi) \, d\psi$$

$$= 2\pi i^n A \sin C \, J_n \left(\frac{\omega \rho \sin C}{v} \right) \cos n\phi$$
$$\times \exp i\omega \left(t - \frac{z \cos C}{v} \right). \quad (4.17)$$

On putting $\beta = (\omega/v) \cos C$ and with suitable choice of A
the expression becomes that given for E_z in an E_n wave,
(2.24). The correct values for the components E_ρ and
E_ϕ also appear on integration of $E_x' \cos \psi \cos n(\phi + \psi)$ and
$E_x' \sin \psi \cos n(\phi + \psi)$ respectively. The magnetic vectors
of these elementary waves lie in a plane normal to the tube
axis, and the electric vectors and directions of propagation
generate the two reciprocal cones shown in Figure 24(b).
For the zero-order wave types the amplitude distribution
of the elementary waves is constant around the cone; for
higher-order types the amplitudes are chosen to vary
harmonically around the cone. For all types the angle C
of the cone of elementary wave directions is given by
$\beta = (\omega/v) \cos C$, or $\cos C = \{1 - (f_0/f)^2\}^{\frac{1}{2}} = \lambda/\lambda_t$, so that
again the critical frequency corresponds to a state when
elementary waves are directed normal to the tube walls,
and are there reflected normally without progressing.

Page and Adams [6] have shown how to use this synthetic
method to determine wave types in polygonal tubes.

CHAPTER V

WAVE GUIDES AS RESONATORS

THE forms of wave guide so far studied are infinitely extended surfaces inside which waves are propagated. If such a wave guide is limited by closing the ends of a finite length of tube in conducting surfaces, a system of standing waves can be set up in the bounded space. Resonators of this type in which oscillation takes place within a bounded space are called cavity or *Hohlraum* resonators. The simpler geometric shapes are readily treated on the lines already used for the investigation of propagation in infinite hollow tubes.

As with transmission in wave guides the results for loss-free conductors have long been known. It is only recently, however, that attention has been paid to the damping effect produced by conductor losses [41], [44], [47], [48]. The treatment of damping used in this chapter is based on that given by Borgnis [44].

ENERGY RELATIONS

The stored energy in an oscillation field is the sum of electric and magnetic contributions having energy densities whose mean values are given by $\varepsilon E \cdot E^*/16\pi$ and $\mu H \cdot H^*/16\pi$. The mean electric and magnetic energies in the volume τ of the resonator are

$$\bar{W}_e = \frac{\varepsilon}{16\pi} \int_\tau E \cdot E^* d\tau, \qquad \bar{W}_m = \frac{\mu}{16\pi} \int_\tau H \cdot H^* d\tau.$$

73

By Maxwell's equations (1.1) their difference is

$$\bar{W}_m - \bar{W}_e = \frac{1}{16\pi}\int_\tau \left[\frac{c}{i\omega}\, H \cdot \operatorname{curl} E^* + \frac{c}{i\omega}\, E \cdot \operatorname{curl} H^* \right] d\tau,$$

and, since the energies are real quantities,

$$\frac{E \cdot \operatorname{curl} H^*}{i\omega} = \frac{E^* \cdot \operatorname{curl} H}{-i\omega}.$$

Hence $\bar{W}_m - \bar{W}_e = \dfrac{c}{16\pi i\omega}\displaystyle\int_\tau (H \cdot \operatorname{curl} E^* - E^* \cdot \operatorname{curl} H)\, d\tau$

$$= \frac{c}{16\pi i\omega}\int_\tau \operatorname{div}(E^* \times H)\, d\tau$$

$$= \frac{c}{16\pi i\omega}\int_S (E^* \times H) \cdot dS, \text{ by Gauss's}$$
theorem,

the last integral being taken over the inner surface of the resonator. For a perfect conductor, E is normal, and H tangential to the surface; thus there is no component of $E^* \times H$ normal to the surface, and the surface integral vanishes. The mean electric and magnetic energies are therefore equal, and the total energy $\bar{W}$ is given by

$$\bar{W} = 2\bar{W}_m = 2\bar{W}_e$$

$$= \frac{\mu}{8\pi}\int_\tau H \cdot H^* d\tau = \frac{\varepsilon}{8\pi}\int_\tau E \cdot E^* d\tau. \quad . \quad (5.1)$$

Oscillations set up in a cavity enclosed by a conductor of high, but finite, conductivity will decrease in amplitude on account of energy dissipated in the metal. The natural logarithm of the ratio of the amplitudes of two successive oscillations is called the logarithmic decrement δ of the resonator. If $\bar{W}(t)$ is the mean electromagnetic energy at time t, and the period of the oscillation $T = 2\pi/\omega$, then

$$\delta = \tfrac{1}{2} \log \frac{\bar{W}(t)}{\bar{W}(t + T)}$$
$$\simeq \tfrac{1}{2} \log \frac{\bar{W}(t)}{\bar{W}(t) + T\,\partial\bar{W}(t)/\partial t} \simeq -\frac{T}{2\bar{W}} \frac{\partial\bar{W}}{\partial t},$$

whence, putting the mean rate of dissipation of energy, $-\partial\bar{W}/\partial t$, equal to $\bar{P}$,

$$\delta = \frac{T\bar{P}}{2\bar{W}} = \frac{\pi}{\omega} \frac{\bar{P}}{\bar{W}}. \quad . \quad . \quad . \quad . \quad (5.2)$$

The parameter Q is often used as a measure of the efficiency of a resonant circuit, and this is related to the logarithmic decrement by the relation $Q = \pi/\delta$. Hence

$$Q = \frac{\omega\bar{W}}{\bar{P}} \quad . \quad . \quad . \quad . \quad . \quad . \quad . \quad (5.3)$$

$$= \frac{\omega \times \text{total electromagnetic energy averaged over one cycle}}{\text{energy lost in unit time}}.$$

For a series resonant circuit of inductance, resistance and capacity, Q takes the familiar form $Q = \omega L/R$. The mean power dissipated in heat per unit of surface area is given by (3.4), and $\bar{P}$ is the integral of this over the surface S,

$$\bar{P} = \frac{c}{16\pi}\left(\frac{\mu_1 f}{\sigma_1}\right)^{\tfrac{1}{2}} \int_S H_S \cdot H_S^* dS. \quad . \quad . \quad (5.4)$$

RECTANGULAR BOX RESONATOR

If, in a rectangular wave guide, waves travelling in both directions along the axis are superposed, a system of standing waves is set up, of which the wavelength measured in the guide, λ_t, is given by (1.14). It will then generally be possible to isolate a section of tube of length l within plane conducting ends without disturbing the field distribution if this length is such that $l = \frac{1}{2}\nu\lambda_t$, $\nu = 1,2,3 \ldots$ The characteristic oscillation frequencies of the resonator thus formed are then determined from (1.14) by

$$f_{mn\nu} = \frac{v}{2}\left[\left(\frac{m}{a}\right)^2 + \left(\frac{n}{b}\right)^2 + \left(\frac{\nu}{l}\right)^2\right]^{\frac{1}{2}} \cdot \cdot \cdot \quad (5.5)$$

Corresponding to the two types of travelling wave, there exist E and H types of standing wave.

E Waves. The field components for an E wave in the resonator are found by adding to those of (1.16) a similar set in which β is replaced by $-\beta$. Then

$$\left.\begin{aligned}
E_z &= \sin\frac{m\pi x}{a}\sin\frac{n\pi y}{b}\cos\frac{\nu\pi z}{l} \\
E_x &= -\frac{1}{k^2}\frac{m\pi}{a}\frac{\nu\pi}{l}\cos\frac{m\pi x}{a}\sin\frac{n\pi y}{b}\sin\frac{\nu\pi z}{l} \\
E_y &= -\frac{1}{k^2}\frac{n\pi}{b}\frac{\nu\pi}{l}\sin\frac{m\pi x}{a}\cos\frac{n\pi y}{b}\sin\frac{\nu\pi z}{l} \\
H_z &= 0 \\
H_x &= \frac{i\omega\varepsilon}{k^2 c}\frac{n\pi}{b}\sin\frac{m\pi x}{a}\cos\frac{n\pi y}{b}\cos\frac{\nu\pi z}{l} \\
H_y &= -\frac{i\omega\varepsilon}{k^2 c}\frac{m\pi}{a}\cos\frac{m\pi x}{a}\sin\frac{n\pi y}{b}\cos\frac{\nu\pi z}{l},
\end{aligned}\right\} \cdot \quad (5.6)$$

k^2 being given as before by $(m\pi/a)^2 + (n\pi/b)^2$. The values of m, n, ν, which are given by a number triplet (used as a suffix when necessary), define in (5.5) an infinite number of possible modes of oscillation, of which usually those of lowest order only will be of interest. Reference to the set of field components (5.6) shows that there are no waves of types (000), (001), (010), (100), (101), (011).

The lowest mode physically possible is that of type (110), for which the characteristic frequency is

$$f_{110} = \frac{v}{2}\left(\frac{1}{a^2} + \frac{1}{b^2}\right)^{\frac{1}{2}}. \quad . \quad . \quad . \quad . \quad (5.7)$$

To find the Q of the resonator, $\bar{W}$ and $\bar{P}$ are calculated from (5.1) and (5.4);

$$\bar{W} = \frac{\mu}{8\pi} \int_0^a \int_0^b \int_0^l (H_x H_x{}^* + H_y H_y{}^*) dx\,dy\,dz$$

$$= \frac{\pi\omega^2\varepsilon^2\mu abl}{64c^2k^4}\left[\left(\frac{m}{a}\right)^2 + \left(\frac{n}{b}\right)^2\right], \quad \text{if } m,\,n,\,v \neq 0.$$

$$\bar{P} = \frac{c}{8\pi}\left(\frac{\mu_1 f}{\sigma_1}\right)^{\frac{1}{2}}\left[\int_0^b\int_0^l (H_y H_y{}^*)_{x=0} dy\,dz + \int_0^l\int_0^a (H_x H_x{}^*)_{y=0} dz\,dx\right.$$

$$\left. + \int_0^a\int_0^b (H_x H_x{}^* + H_y H_y{}^*)_{z=0} dx\,dy\right]$$

$$= \frac{\pi\omega^2\varepsilon^2}{32ck^4}\left(\frac{\mu_1 f}{\sigma_1}\right)^{\frac{1}{2}}\left[b(a+l)\left(\frac{m}{a}\right)^2 + a(b+l)\left(\frac{n}{b}\right)^2\right], \text{ if } m,n,v \neq 0.$$

Whence, by (5.3),

$$Q_{mnv} = \frac{\pi\mu}{c}\left(\frac{\sigma_1 f_{mnv}}{\mu_1}\right)^{\frac{1}{2}}\frac{\left(\dfrac{m}{a}\right)^2 + \left(\dfrac{n}{b}\right)^2}{\left(\dfrac{m}{a}\right)^2\left(\dfrac{1}{a} + \dfrac{1}{l}\right) + \left(\dfrac{n}{b}\right)^2\left(\dfrac{1}{b} + \dfrac{1}{l}\right)}. \quad . \quad (5.8)$$

These results do not hold if m, n, or v is zero. The only case to be considered is that where $v = 0$; $m,\,n \neq 0$. Then the value of Q is found to be

$$Q_{mn0} = \frac{2\pi\mu}{c}\left(\frac{\sigma_1 f_{mn0}}{\mu_1}\right)^{\frac{1}{2}}\frac{\left(\dfrac{m}{a}\right)^2 + \left(\dfrac{n}{b}\right)^2}{\left(\dfrac{m}{a}\right)^2\left(\dfrac{2}{a} + \dfrac{1}{l}\right) + \left(\dfrac{n}{b}\right)^2\left(\dfrac{2}{b} + \dfrac{1}{l}\right)}. \quad . \quad (5.9)$$

If the box is cubical the expressions are considerably simplified. It is noteworthy that, for the type (mn0), the resonant frequency is independent of the dimension *l*, although the Q increases with *l* from zero to an asymptotic value.

H Waves. For H waves the field components, obtained by superposing on the solution (1.18) a wave travelling in the direction of $-z$, are

$$
\left.\begin{aligned}
H_z &= \cos\frac{m\pi x}{a}\cos\frac{n\pi y}{b}\sin\frac{\nu\pi z}{l} \\[4pt]
H_x &= -\frac{1}{k^2}\frac{m\pi}{a}\frac{\nu\pi}{l}\sin\frac{m\pi x}{a}\cos\frac{n\pi y}{b}\cos\frac{\nu\pi z}{l} \\[4pt]
H_y &= -\frac{1}{k^2}\frac{n\pi}{b}\frac{\nu\pi}{l}\cos\frac{m\pi x}{a}\sin\frac{n\pi y}{b}\cos\frac{\nu\pi z}{l} \\[4pt]
E_z &= 0 \\[4pt]
E_x &= \frac{i\omega\mu}{ck^2}\frac{n\pi}{b}\cos\frac{m\pi x}{a}\sin\frac{n\pi y}{b}\sin\frac{\nu\pi z}{l} \\[4pt]
E_y &= -\frac{i\omega\mu}{ck^2}\frac{m\pi}{a}\sin\frac{m\pi x}{a}\cos\frac{n\pi y}{b}\sin\frac{\nu\pi z}{l}.
\end{aligned}\right\} \quad (5.10)
$$

In (5.10) the origin has been moved a distance $l/2\nu$ along the z-axis in order to make the plane $z = 0$ a nodal plane for E_x and E_y and so allow this to be an end plane of

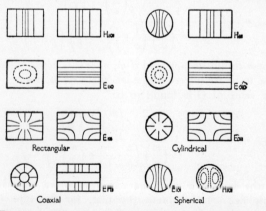

FIG. 25.—Modes of oscillation in cavity resonators.
Full lines, electric force ; dashed lines, magnetic force

the resonator. The characteristic frequencies are the same as those for E type oscillations given by (5.5). Hence the lowest modes are (011) and (101). These can be regarded as fundamental E waves in which the longitudinal component is directed along the x- and y-axes respectively, and for them the Q is obtained from (5.9) by suitable interchange of the dimensions.

Sketches of the simpler field patterns are given in Figure 25.

CYLINDRICAL RESONATOR

The properties of a cylindrical resonator of radius a and length l can also be derived by superposition from the study of cylindrical wave guides.

E Waves. Resonance occurs when $l = \frac{1}{2}v\lambda_t$, and, as λ_t is given by (2.21), this defines the frequencies

$$f_{nmv} = \frac{v}{2}\left[\left(\frac{k_{nm}}{\pi}\right)^2 + \left(\frac{v}{l}\right)^2\right]^{\frac{1}{2}}, \quad . \quad . \quad . \quad (5.11)$$

$k_{nm}a$ being the mth zero of $J_n(ka) = 0$, of which numerical values have been given in Table 1 (p. 28). Deriving the field as before from (2.24), we have

$$\left.\begin{array}{l} E_z = k^2 J_n(k\rho) \cos n\phi \cos \dfrac{v\pi z}{l} \\[2mm] E_\rho = -\dfrac{v\pi k}{l} J_n'(k\rho) \cos n\phi \sin \dfrac{v\pi z}{l} \\[2mm] E_\phi = \dfrac{nv\pi}{l\rho} J_n(k\rho) \sin n\phi \sin \dfrac{v\pi z}{l} \\[2mm] H_z = 0 \\[2mm] H_\rho = -\dfrac{i\omega\varepsilon n}{c\rho} J_n(k\rho) \sin n\phi \cos \dfrac{v\pi z}{l} \\[2mm] H_\phi = -\dfrac{i\omega\varepsilon k}{c} J_n'(k\rho) \cos n\phi \cos \dfrac{v\pi z}{l} \end{array}\right\} \quad . \quad (5.12)$$

From these it is seen that it is possible for v to be zero, resulting in a field with its electric vector entirely in the axial direction and of frequency independent of the length of the resonator. The smallest value of k is k_{01}, and the frequency of the fundamental oscillation is

$$f_{010} = \frac{vk_{01}}{2\pi} = \frac{2 \cdot 405 v}{2\pi a}. \quad \cdots \quad (5.13)$$

The stored energy in the resonator and the rate of dissipation of it are determined from the field components with the aid of (3.12); they give as the values of Q

$$Q_{nmv} = \frac{2\pi\mu}{c}\left(\frac{\sigma_1 f_{nmv}}{\mu_1}\right)^{\frac{1}{2}} \frac{1}{\dfrac{1}{a}+\dfrac{2}{l}}, \quad v \neq 0 \quad . \quad (5.14)$$

If v is zero, as for the fundamental oscillation (010), Q is given by

$$Q_{nm0} = \frac{2\pi\mu}{c}\left(\frac{\sigma_1 f_{nm0}}{\mu_1}\right)^{\frac{1}{2}} \frac{1}{\dfrac{1}{a}+\dfrac{1}{l}}. \quad \cdots \quad (5.15)$$

While, for $(nm0)$ oscillations, the frequency is independent of the length of the cylinder, the Q varies from zero to an asymptotic value as l increases from zero to an infinite value.

H Waves. For H type oscillations in a cylindrical resonator the resonance frequencies are defined by the equation (5.11) in which k_{nm} now has values such that $k_{nm}a$ is the mth zero of $J_n'(ka) = 0$. The field components, derived as before from (2.25), are

$$\left.\begin{aligned}
H_z &= k^2 J_n(k\rho) \cos n\phi \sin \frac{v\pi z}{l} \\[4pt]
H_\rho &= \frac{v\pi k}{l} J_n'(k\rho) \cos n\phi \cos \frac{v\pi z}{l} \\[4pt]
H_\phi &= -\frac{nv\pi}{l\rho} J_n(k\rho) \sin n\phi \cos \frac{v\pi z}{l} \\[4pt]
E_z &= 0 \\[4pt]
E_\rho &= \frac{i\omega\mu n}{\rho c} J_n(k\rho) \sin n\phi \sin \frac{v\pi z}{l} \\[4pt]
E_\phi &= \frac{i\omega\mu k}{c} J_n'(k\rho) \cos n\phi \sin \frac{v\pi z}{l}.
\end{aligned}\right\} \quad . \quad (5.16)$$

Of the oscillation modes defined by the triplet (nmv) those which have $v = 0$ do not exist. Reference to Table 1 shows that the lowest mode is (111) and for this the frequency is

$$f_{111} = \frac{v}{2}\left[\left(\frac{1\cdot 84}{\pi a}\right)^2 + \frac{1}{l^2}\right]^{\frac{1}{2}}. \quad . \quad . \quad . \quad (5.17)$$

Whether or not this frequency is lower than the fundamental E_{010} type depends on the relative values of a and l.

The Q for the H modes is found to be the rather complicated expression

$$Q_{nmv} = \frac{2\pi\mu}{c}\left(\frac{\sigma_1 f_{nmv}}{\mu_1}\right)^{\frac{1}{2}} \frac{a\left[k_{nm}^2 + \left(\frac{v\pi}{l}\right)^2\right]\left[1 - \left(\frac{n}{k_{nm}a}\right)^2\right]}{k_{nm}^2 + \frac{2v^2\pi^2 a}{l^3} + \frac{n^2 v^2 \pi^2}{k_{nm}^2 a l^2}\left(\frac{1}{a} - \frac{2}{l}\right)} . \quad (5.18)$$

Considerable simplification is obtained in the particular case of $l = 2a$, when the expression becomes

$$Q_{nmv} = \frac{2\pi\mu a}{c}\left(\frac{\sigma_1 f_{nmv}}{\mu_1}\right)^{\frac{1}{2}}\left[1 - \left(\frac{n}{k_{nm}a}\right)^2\right] \quad . \quad . \quad (5.19)$$

Figure 25 shows field distributions of a few modes of oscillation.

SPHERICAL RESONATOR

The spherical cavity resonator is another simple geometrical shape which can readily be treated in terms of spherical polar coordinates r, θ, ϕ. Solutions of the vector wave equation in spherical polars have already been obtained and applied to wave transmission in a conical horn. The functions U, V from which the fields are derived are solutions of (2.46); one form of the solution has already been indicated, but for a spherical cavity we require a solution which is finite at $r = 0$ as well as at the poles $\theta = 0, \pi$. These requirements are fulfilled in the solution

$$U, V = r^{\frac{1}{2}} J_{n+\frac{1}{2}}(\omega r/v) P_n^m(\cos\theta) \cos m\phi, \quad . \quad . \quad (5.20)$$

in which m and n are integers, and $m < n$. The field equations for E and H type oscillations derived from these are the same as those given in (2.48) and (2.49) except that $H_{n+\frac{1}{2}}^{(2)}$ is replaced by $J_{n+\frac{1}{2}}$, i.e. a cylinder function suitable for the representation of stationary waves replaces one indicating travelling waves. The presence of a radial component of electric or magnetic field is seen to be the characteristic of E and H oscillations. Application of boundary conditions to the field components gives relations determining the modes of oscillation.

E Waves. The conditions to be fulfilled at the surface of a spherical cavity of radius a, i.e. $E_\theta = E_\phi = 0$ for $r = a$, require that

$$\left[\frac{d}{dr}\{r^{\frac{1}{2}} J_{n+\frac{1}{2}}(\omega r/v)\}\right]_{r=a} = 0. \quad . \quad . \quad (5.21)$$

By the use of (3.10) this condition becomes

$$\frac{J_{n+\frac{1}{2}}(\omega a/v)}{J_{n-\frac{1}{2}}(\omega a/v)} = \frac{\omega a}{vn}. \quad . \quad . \quad (5.22)$$

The solutions of (5.22) determine the characteristic oscillation frequencies $f_{n\nu}$, ν indicating the νth root of (5.22). These frequencies, since they do not involve m, are independent of the distribution in ϕ. The wave types are distinguished by the number triplet $(nm\nu)$, m being restricted to those integral values where $m < n$. Bessel functions whose order is half an odd integer can be expressed in terms of trigonometric functions. For $n = 1$, those involved are

$$J_{\frac{1}{2}}(x) = (2/\pi x)^{\frac{1}{2}} \sin x,$$

and

$$J_{\frac{3}{2}}(x) = (2/\pi x)^{\frac{1}{2}}\{(1/x)\sin x - \cos x\},$$

so that (5.22) becomes, putting $\omega a/v = \zeta$,

$$\tan\zeta = \frac{\zeta}{1 - \zeta^2}.$$

The first root of this equation is $\zeta_{11} = 2\cdot74$, giving for the fundamental frequency

$$f_{11} = \frac{2\cdot74 v}{2\pi a}. \quad \cdots \quad (5.23)$$

The field of type (101), which has f_{11} as its characteristic frequency, is

$$\left.\begin{aligned}
E_r &= \frac{2}{r^{\frac{3}{2}}} J_{\frac{3}{2}}\left(\frac{\omega}{v}r\right)\cos\theta \\
E_\theta &= -\frac{1}{r}\frac{d}{dr}\left[r^{\frac{1}{2}}J_{\frac{3}{2}}\left(\frac{\omega}{v}r\right)\right]\sin\theta \\
H_\phi &= \frac{i\omega\varepsilon}{cr^{\frac{1}{2}}}J_{\frac{3}{2}}\left(\frac{\omega}{v}r\right)\sin\theta.
\end{aligned}\right\} \quad (5.24)$$

The lines of force in a meridian plane are shown in Figure 25.

Other solutions of (5.22) are given by

$$\begin{array}{llll}
\zeta_{11} & 2\cdot74 & \zeta_{12} & 6\cdot12 \\
\zeta_{21} & 3\cdot87 & \cdots & \\
\zeta_{31} & 8\cdot72 & \cdots &
\end{array}$$

The Q of the spherical resonator is calculated from the field equations, with the assistance of the relation

$$\int_0^\pi \left[\left(\frac{dP_n^m}{d\theta}\right)^2 + \frac{m^2}{\sin^2\theta}(P_n^m)^2\right]\sin\theta\,d\theta = \frac{2n(n+1)}{2n+1}\frac{(n+m)!}{(n-m)!}. \quad (5.25)$$

Then

$$Q_{n\nu} = \frac{2\pi\mu a}{c}\left(\frac{\sigma_1 f_{n\nu}}{\mu_1}\right)^{\frac{1}{2}}\left[1 - \frac{n(n+1)}{\zeta_{n\nu}^2}\right]. \quad (5.26)$$

H Waves. Equations (2.49), with $H_{n+\frac{1}{2}}^{(2)}$ replaced by $J_{n+\frac{1}{2}}$, show that the boundary conditions for H-type oscillations require that

$$J_{n+\frac{1}{2}}\left(\frac{\omega}{v}a\right) = 0. \quad \cdots \quad (5.27)$$

The fundamental frequency is again f_{11}, and for this (5.27) reduces, with $\omega a/v = \zeta$, to

$$\tan\zeta = \zeta,$$

of which the first root is $\zeta_{11} = 4 \cdot 49$. Hence the lowest mode has a frequency

$$f_{11} = \frac{4 \cdot 49 v}{2\pi a}. \qquad \cdots \cdots \quad (5.28)$$

For this type the field components become

$$
\left.
\begin{aligned}
H_r &= \frac{2}{r^{\frac{3}{2}}} J_{\frac{3}{2}}\!\left(\frac{\omega}{v} r\right) \cos \theta \\
H_\theta &= -\frac{1}{r} \frac{d}{dr}\!\left[r^{\frac{1}{2}} J_{\frac{3}{2}}\!\left(\frac{\omega}{v} r\right) \right] \sin \theta \\
E_\phi &= -\frac{i\omega\mu}{cr^{\frac{1}{2}}} J_{\frac{3}{2}}\!\left(\frac{\omega}{v} r\right) \sin \theta.
\end{aligned}
\right\} \qquad (5.29)
$$

This field of force is depicted in Figure 25.

Other solutions of (5.27), determining characteristic frequencies, are

$$
\begin{array}{llll}
\zeta_{11} & 4 \cdot 49 & \zeta_{12} & 7 \cdot 72 \\
\zeta_{21} & 5 \cdot 76 & \cdots & \\
\zeta_{31} & 6 \cdot 99 & \cdots &
\end{array}
$$

The Q for H oscillations is given by the simple expression

$$Q_{nv} = \frac{2\pi\mu a}{c}\left(\frac{\sigma_1 f_{nv}}{\mu_1}\right)^{\frac{1}{2}}. \qquad \cdots \quad (5.30)$$

COAXIAL RESONATOR

The most familiar type of cavity resonator is a length of coaxial line closed at each end, oscillating in a principal transverse mode. For a cavity of length l the resonant frequencies are $f_n = nv/2l$, with $n = 1, 2, 3, \ldots$, and the field, derived by superposition from (2.31), is

$$E_\rho = \frac{1}{\rho} \sin \frac{n\pi z}{l}, \quad H_\phi = \frac{i}{\rho}\left(\frac{\varepsilon}{\mu}\right)^{\frac{1}{2}} \cos \frac{n\pi z}{l} . \qquad (5.31)$$

When the radii of the outer and inner conductors are

a and b, the Q of the coaxial resonator oscillating in a principal mode is

$$Q_n = \frac{4\pi\mu a}{c}\left(\frac{\sigma_1 f_n}{\mu_1}\right)^{\frac{1}{2}} \frac{\log (a/b)}{1 + a/b + 4(a/l)\log (a/b)} \cdot \quad (5.32)$$

For a given radius of outer conductor this has a maximum value when $a/b = 3{\cdot}6$, for which it becomes

$$Q_n = \frac{4\pi\mu a}{c}\left(\frac{\sigma_1 f_n}{\mu_1}\right)^{\frac{1}{2}} \frac{1}{3{\cdot}6 + 4a/l} \cdot \quad \cdot \quad \cdot \quad (5.33)$$

Oscillations depending on the complementary waves discussed in Chapter II can also occur, but normally they will be of frequencies much higher than the principal oscillation. For these, papers by Kalähne [39], and Barrow and Mieher [49] may be consulted.

Oscillation frequencies of other forms of resonator, such as ellipsoids [84] and concentric spheres, have been discussed by various authors, to whom reference will be found in Bateman's *Electrical and Optical Wave Motion*. For the more complicated shapes approximation methods have to be employed. One method [81, 101] is to divide the cavity into regions for each of which solutions can be obtained, and then superpose solutions so as to match the fields at the boundaries. An alternative is Southwell's relaxation method [93].

COMPARISON OF RESONATORS

For purposes of comparison the results have been summarised for some particular cases in Table 2. The free-space wavelengths of the fundamental oscillations of air-filled copper resonators are tabulated, σ_1 for copper being given the value $6 \times 10^{-4}c^2$ e.s.u. For the values of Q given, λ and a are in centimetres. It will be seen that, for a given wavelength, the most efficient resonator of those studied is the sphere oscillating in its lowest H mode, and this is the largest in dimensions. Corresponding to the low attenuation constant associated with the H_0 mode in a cylindrical guide, the Q of the H_{011} mode in a cylindrical resonator is also high. The effect of small ellipticity has been calculated by Kinzer and Wilson [94].

The excitation of these resonators may be by means of a probe carrying high frequency currents inserted along a line of electric force, or by a loop encircling magnetic

TABLE 2

	Cube: (sides a)	Cylinder: (radius a; length $2a$)			Coaxial Cylinders (radii a, $a/3 \cdot 6$; length $2a$)	Sphere (radius a)	
	E_{110}, H_{011}	E_{010}	H_{111}	H_{011}	Transverse	E_{1m1}	H_{1m1}
λ	$1 \cdot 41a$	$2 \cdot 61a$	$2 \cdot 60a$	$1 \cdot 52a$	$4a$	$2 \cdot 29a$	$1 \cdot 40a$
$Q \times 10^{-3}$	$\begin{cases} 6 \cdot 28 \sqrt{\lambda} \\ 7 \cdot 47 \sqrt{a} \end{cases}$	$\begin{cases} 6 \cdot 80 \sqrt{\lambda} \\ 11 \cdot 0 \sqrt{a} \end{cases}$	$\begin{cases} 7 \cdot 24 \sqrt{\lambda} \\ 11 \cdot 7 \sqrt{a} \end{cases}$	$\begin{cases} 17 \cdot 5 \sqrt{\lambda} \\ 21 \cdot 7 \sqrt{a} \end{cases}$	$\begin{cases} 2 \cdot 38 \sqrt{\lambda} \\ 4 \cdot 76 \sqrt{a} \end{cases}$	$\begin{cases} 8 \cdot 53 \sqrt{\lambda} \\ 12 \cdot 9 \sqrt{a} \end{cases}$	$\begin{cases} 19 \cdot 0 \sqrt{\lambda} \\ 22 \cdot 5 \sqrt{a} \end{cases}$

lines, or possibly by an electron stream where the resonator is an integral part of an electronic oscillator. Any form of coupling will involve some aperture which may alter profoundly the damping of the resonator. Calculations of the input impedance of cavity resonators when excited by a probe or a coupling loop have been made by Condon [51] and Bernier [92]. Excitation through a small hole from a wave guide field is another common method. The dependence on hole diameter has been calculated by Bethe [97], whose formula shows that, with certain limitations, the power transmitted through a hole of radius a is proportional to a^6.

Given a path Γ joining two points inside a cavity, for each mode of oscillation an equivalent parallel circuit of inductance, capacity, and resistance can be uniquely determined, with the same Q value, and such that the potential difference across it is equal to the integral $-\int_\Gamma E \cdot ds$ of the field in the cavity. The value of this shunt resistance is a useful parameter ; it is usually chosen for a path which gives the maximum potential difference across the cavity.

If V is the potential difference across the equivalent circuit and R its shunt resistance, then the power dissipated at resonance is $V^2/2R$. If this is equated to the power $\bar{P}$ dissipated in the cavity, then, through the definition of Q-factor,

$$R = \frac{Q[\int_\Gamma E \cdot ds]^2}{2\omega \bar{W}} \text{ e.s.u.}$$

$$= 60\lambda Q\left(\frac{\mu}{\varepsilon}\right)^{\frac{1}{2}} \frac{[\int_\Gamma E \cdot ds]^2}{\int_\tau E \cdot E^* d\tau} \text{ ohms.} \quad . \quad . \quad (5.34)$$

For a rectangular resonator in the E_{110} mode, if the integration path is taken as a straight line joining the centres of the end faces, the equivalent resistance is given by

$$R = 480 Q\left(\frac{\mu}{\varepsilon}\right)^{\frac{1}{2}} \frac{l}{(a^2 + b^2)^{\frac{1}{2}}} \text{ ohms.} \quad . \quad . \quad (5.35)$$

For a cylindrical resonator in the E_{010} mode, the resistance is

$$R = \left(\frac{\mu}{\varepsilon}\right)^{\frac{1}{2}} \frac{60\lambda Q l}{\pi a^2 \{J_0'(ka)\}^2} = 185 Q\left(\frac{\mu}{\varepsilon}\right)^{\frac{1}{2}} \frac{l}{a} \text{ ohms,} \quad (5.36)$$

the path being the axis of the cylinder.

CHAPTER VI

WAVE GUIDES AS RADIATORS

When waves are excited within a wave guide which is open at one end they travel along the guide, and, on reaching the open end, are radiated into free space. This radiated energy is more or less concentrated into a beam, and under suitable conditions the system may act as an efficient directional radiator. This property of the wave guide was demonstrated by Sir Oliver Lodge [1] at the Royal Institution in 1894, but no further work appears to have been done until forty years later, when some measurements on radiation patterns were made by Bergmann and Krügel [52]. Since the renaissance of wave guides in 1936 much work, theoretical and practical, has been done on their radiating properties, particularly by Barrow and his collaborators at the Massachusetts Institute of Technology, and various forms of wave guide have been shown to be efficient directional radiators for very short wavelengths.

THE RADIATION PROBLEM

The difficulties involved in the theoretical treatment of radiation from wave guides are considerable, and the procedure can be dealt with here only in outline. The problem is a diffraction one ; a wave passes through an aperture of given shape into free space, and thereby suffers diffraction. It is required to find the amplitude distribution at a distance from the aperture. For similar optical problems the classical Huygens-Kirchhoff formula, although involving considerable assumptions, has given solutions in satisfactory agreement with observed results.

The procedure is to choose a surface S, of which the aperture forms a part, the remainder being an opaque screen. The dielectric is assumed to be air, and ω/c is replaced by h. If w is a solution of the scalar wave equation $(\nabla^2 + h^2)w = 0$, r is the distance of a surface element from a fixed point P inside S, and $\partial/\partial n$ denotes differentiation along the outward normal to S, then the amplitude at P, expressed as an integral of the amplitude over the surface S, is given by

$$w_P = \frac{1}{4\pi} \int_S \left[\frac{e^{-ihr}}{r} \frac{\partial w}{\partial n} - w \frac{\partial}{\partial n}\left(\frac{e^{-ihr}}{r} \right) \right] dS. \quad . \quad (6.1)$$

This is a particular case, due to Helmholz, of Kirchhoff's formula.

Values of w over the surface will not be known exactly, and suitable values must be assumed. It is usual to suppose, as did Kirchhoff, that the value of w over the aperture is that which would exist if the screen were not present, and that w and $\partial w/\partial n$ are zero on the screen itself. Strictly, these assumptions are invalid, since they imply discontinuities at the boundary of the aperture inconsistent with Green's theorem upon which (6.1) depends. Invalid also is the use of a single scalar wave function to represent an electromagnetic wave. Where the wavelength is small in comparison with the opening, the assumption of zero intensity on the shadow surface of the screen is approximately true, and if, as in most optical problems, the intensity and not the polarization is required, one scalar function suffices. However, for a wave guide having an opening comparable with the wavelength, the diffraction pattern is much broader, and intensities on the outside of the tube—which forms the screen—may be not even approximately zero. It is also necessary to have a vector solution which will give the polarization of the diffracted wave. If (6.1) is applied to each Cartesian component of E and H with the assump-

7

tion of discontinuous values at the boundary of the aperture, the result is found to be inconsistent with Maxwell's equations, giving a non-transverse radiation field, which is physically impossible. Kottler [64] has given an expression which is a vector analogue of Kirchhoff's formula, and this has been adopted by Stratton and Chu [58] for the treatment of wave-guide problems. Bethe [97] and Smythe [100], however, have pointed out that terms in this solution violate the requirement that the electric field must be normal to the conducting screen. Smythe's approach seems the simplest and most satisfactory so far. Treating an aperture in a plane conducting screen, he shows that the radiation field is the same as would exist if screen and aperture were replaced by a double current sheet fitting the aperture, the current distribution being readily calculable. By this means the expression for the diffracted electric field at an external point P is found to be

$$2\pi E_P = \int_S (\boldsymbol{n} \times \boldsymbol{E}) \times \boldsymbol{i}_r \frac{\partial}{\partial r}\left(\frac{e^{-ihr}}{r}\right) dS, \quad . \quad (6.2)$$

where $\boldsymbol{E}$ is the tangential field in the aperture S, $\boldsymbol{n}$ a unit vector along the normal to S, and $\boldsymbol{i}_r$ a unit vector in the direction of $\boldsymbol{r}$, both $\boldsymbol{n}$ and $\boldsymbol{i}_r$ being directed away from P.

In the application of (6.2) to particular apertures, a spherical coordinate system is adopted for the radiated wave, and considerable simplification is obtained by assuming that the distance of the point P from the aperture is large compared with the other dimensions involved. In the absence of knowledge of the exact value of E over the open end of a guide coinciding with the aperture we assume the unperturbed value which would exist in a continuous guide. This is found to predict radiation patterns with considerable accuracy.

RADIATION FROM RECTANGULAR WAVE GUIDE

Figure 26 shows the coordinate system for a rectangular tube, in which $r \simeq R - \sin\theta(x\cos\phi + y\sin\phi)$. Taking the electric vector of an H_{10} wave at the aperture as having its unperturbed value $E_y = E_0 \sin (\pi x/a)$, then the triple

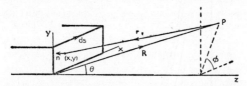

FIG. 26.—Coordinate system for radiation formulae.

vector product in (6.2) has the value

$$(\boldsymbol{n} \times \boldsymbol{E}) \times \boldsymbol{i}_r \simeq (jR \cos \theta - kR \sin \theta \sin \phi)\frac{E_0}{R} \sin \frac{\pi x}{a},$$

j and k being unit vectors along the y- and z-axes. A change to spherical coordinates, with $\boldsymbol{i}_\theta$ and $\boldsymbol{i}_\phi$ unit vectors along the θ- and ϕ-axes, gives

$$(\boldsymbol{n} \times \boldsymbol{E}) \times \boldsymbol{i}_r \simeq (\boldsymbol{i}_\theta \sin \phi + \boldsymbol{i}_\phi \cos \theta \cos \phi)\frac{E_0}{R} \sin \frac{\pi x}{a}.$$

The other term in (6.2) is

$$\frac{\partial}{\partial r}\left(\frac{e^{-ihr}}{r}\right) \simeq -\frac{ih}{R} \exp \{- ih(R - x \sin \theta \cos \phi$$
$$- y \sin \theta \sin \phi)\}.$$

Performing the integration, we get

$$E_P = \frac{i\pi ab E_0}{2\lambda R}(\boldsymbol{i}_\theta \sin \phi + \boldsymbol{i}_\phi \cos \theta \cos \phi)$$

$$\times \frac{\cos A}{A^2 - (\pi/2)^2} \frac{\sin B}{B}e_{-i[\omega R/c-(A+B)]}, \quad . \quad (6.3)$$

where $A = (a\pi/\lambda) \sin \theta \cos \phi$, $B = (b\pi/\lambda) \sin \theta \sin \phi$. The form of the beam can be appreciated by considering the horizontal and vertical patterns, for which ϕ is 0 and $\pi/2$ respectively. These patterns, examples of which are shown in Figure 30, consist of a main beam with its

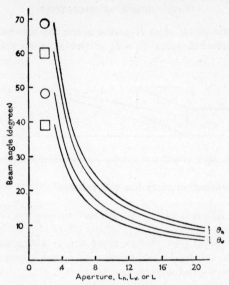

FIG. 27.—Variation of beam angle with aperture for rectangular and circular guides.

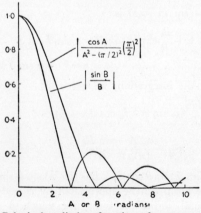

FIG. 28.—Principal radiation functions for rectangular guides.
$A = (a\pi/\lambda) \sin \theta$, $B = (b\pi/\lambda) \sin \theta$.

maximum in the direction of the axis of the guide, and a number of secondary lobes. The sharpness of the main beam is dependent on the angle between the first zeros of intensity on either side of the principal maximum, this being called the *beam angle*. For the horizontal pattern ($\phi = 0$), then, the beam angle is

$$\theta_h = 2 \sin^{-1}(3\lambda/2a) = 2 \sin^{-1}(3/2L_h), \qquad . \quad (6.4)$$

and, in a vertical plane ($\phi = \pi/2$), is

$$\theta_v = 2 \sin^{-1}(\lambda/b) = 2 \sin^{-1}(1/L_v), . \qquad . \quad (6.5)$$

where L_h and L_v represent the horizontal and vertical apertures, a/λ and b/λ. The beam angles in the two planes are variable independently by adjustment of the dimensions a and b, and it will be noted that for a square tube the pattern in the vertical plane (parallel to the electric vector in the tube) is narrower than that in the horizontal plane. Curves showing the relations of beam angle to aperture are given in Figure 27. As an example, a square tube with sides three wavelengths long will produce a beam with a vertical angle of 39° and a horizontal angle of 60°. If the sides a and b are several wavelengths long, $\dfrac{\cos A}{A^2 - (\pi/2)^2}$ and $\dfrac{\sin B}{B}$ in (6.3) are the principal factors determining the beam pattern in the horizontal and vertical planes respectively. Thus the curves of these expressions for $\phi = 0$ and $\phi = \pi/2$, given in Figure 28, show the relative amplitudes of the main and secondary beams, horizontal and vertical. The secondary beams are much larger in the vertical than in the horizontal plane, the heights of the second maxima being $\frac{1}{5}$ and $\frac{1}{14}$ respectively of the principal maximum. Increase of the aperture sharpens the primary beam, but does not appreciably affect the relative magnitudes of the secondary lobes.

Smythe [101] has given a more accurate formula, based on a better approximation to the actual field at the aperture than the unperturbed value assumed here, but the difference is not significant. The expression (6.3) and the earlier formulae of Chu [62] and Schelkunoff [57] differ somewhat in the shape of their beam patterns but not in the position of their zeros.

Another important property of a radiator is its relative power gain. This may be defined as the ratio of the power radiated from an elementary dipole to that radiated from the wave guide to produce, in each case, the same power per unit area at a fixed remote point in the direction of maximum radiation.† If the mean power per unit area received at a distance R from a dipole be unity, the total power, an integration of $\sin^2 \theta$ over the surface of a sphere, is $\frac{8}{3}\pi R^2$. The power per unit area received from the guide is, by Poynting's theorem, $(c/8\pi)E_P \cdot E_P{}^*$, which, by (6.3), has the value at $\theta = 0$

$$\frac{c}{8\pi} \frac{a^2 b^2}{\lambda^2 R^2} E_0{}^2.$$

The total power radiated from the guide is equal to the rate of flow of energy down the tube. This has already been calculated (p. 47) for H_{mn} waves, and the required value for the H_{10} wave is twice that used in (3.8). From these expressions, putting E_0 equal to $-2ia/\lambda$ as in (1.18), the gain relative to an elementary dipole is given by

$$G = \frac{64ab\lambda_t}{3\pi\lambda^3} \simeq 6\cdot 8 \; \frac{\text{area of aperture}}{\lambda^2}, \quad . \quad . \quad (6.6)$$

the approximation assuming that the wavelength is sufficiently below the critical value for $(\lambda/\lambda_0)^2$ to be neglected in comparison with unity. Thus, for example, the power gain of a square wave guide radiator with sides three wavelengths long is about 18 decibels.

† On this basis the power gains of a half-wave dipole and an omnidirectional radiator are $1\cdot 10$ and $3/2\pi$ respectively.

Other types of wave which have more complex field distribution produce, in general, radiation patterns with multiple principal beams, in section similar to those due to a linear radiator excited in its higher modes.

RADIATION FROM CIRCULAR WAVE GUIDE

The wave of lowest critical frequency in the circular guide is the H_{11} type, whose radiated field will now be discussed. This wave is analogous to the H_{10} wave in the rectangular guide, the electric vector being predominantly vertical. From the field equations (2.25), the radiation formula gives for the electric field at P

$$E_P = - \frac{4\pi^2 a}{\lambda^2 R} \left[i_\theta \frac{J_1(D)}{D} \sin \phi + i_\phi \frac{J_1'(D)}{1 - (D/k_{11}a)^2} \cos \theta \cos \phi \right]$$
$$\times J_1(k_{11}a)e^{-ihR}, \quad . \quad (6.7)$$

where $D = (2\pi a/\lambda) \sin \theta$. The beam angle in the horizontal plane ($\phi = 0$) is determined by the first zero of the term $J_1'(D)/\{1 - (D/k_{11}a)^2\}$. This is given by $D = 5 \cdot 33$, so that

$$\theta_h = 2 \sin^{-1} (5 \cdot 33/\pi L) ; \quad . \quad . \quad (6.8)$$

for the vertical plane ($\phi = \pi/2$) the beam angle depends on the first zero of $J_1(D)$, $D = 3 \cdot 83$, and

$$\theta_v = 2 \sin^{-1} (3 \cdot 83/\pi L), \quad . \quad . \quad (6.9)$$

L representing the aperture $2a/\lambda$. The variation of these with L is shown also in Figure 27 ; once more the vertical beam angle is the sharper. Where the beam angle is not too large the functions $\dfrac{J_1'(D)}{1 - (D/k_{11}a)^2}$ and $\dfrac{J_1(D)}{D}$ determine approximately the beam form in the horizontal and vertical planes, and comparison of the curves of these shown in Figure 29 with those of Figure 28 shows that the amplitude of the secondary lobes is considerably smaller for the circular than for the rectangular wave guide radiator, with ratios of second to principal maximum of $\frac{1}{8}$ and $\frac{1}{20}$ in vertical and horizontal planes respectively.

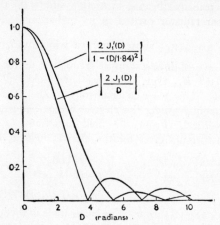

FIG. 29.—Principal radiation functions for circular guides.
$D = (2\pi a/\lambda) \sin \theta$.

The mean power per unit area received at a point distant R along the axis of the tube is, from (6.7),

$$\frac{c\pi^3}{2} \frac{a^2}{\lambda^4 R^2} \{J_1(k_{11}a)\}^2.$$

Taking the expression for $\bar{W}$ used in deriving (3.14) as the power travelling down the tube, the gain over a dipole is

$$G = \frac{16\pi^2 a^2 \lambda_t}{3\lambda^3} \frac{1}{(k_{11}a)^2 - 1} \simeq 7\cdot0 \frac{\text{area of aperture}}{\lambda^2} . \quad . \quad (6.10)$$

A guide of diameter equal to three wavelengths gives beam angles of $48°$ in the vertical plane, $69°$ in the horizontal plane, and a gain of 17 decibels.

Thus for gain and beam width there is little to choose between a circular tube and a square tube of comparable dimensions, but the radiation pattern from the circular tube has smaller secondary lobes. With a rectangular tube it is possible to vary the beam angle independently in horizontal and vertical planes, a property not possessed by the circular tube with its single variable dimension. One or two typical patterns are shown in Figure 30.

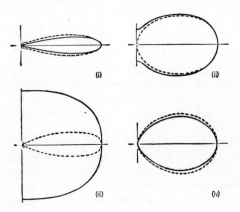

Fig. 30.—Radiation patterns of open-ended guides with plane conducting screen : (i) circular, $a = 2\lambda$; (ii) circular, $a = \lambda/2$; (iii) rectangular, $a = 3\lambda$, $b = \lambda/2$; (iv) rectangular, $a = b = \lambda$.

(Full line, vertical plane ; dashed line, horizontal plane.)

For some details of wave types of higher order the paper by Chu [62] should be consulted. The E_0 and H_0 waves in a circular wave guide give radiation patterns which have zero intensity along the axis, and, in section, show two equal main beams equally inclined to the axis. The higher order wave types have multiple beams and generally show a considerable fraction of the energy diffracted at large angles.

Bethe [97], using essentially the same method as above, has studied the diffraction of plane waves through small holes, and has applied this to consider the excitation of a cavity through a hole and the oscillations of cavities coupled by a hole.

ELECTROMAGNETIC HORNS

The above results have shown that, to obtain a highly directive beam, a large aperture is necessary. This can be provided more economically by flaring the end of a circular or rectangular guide of more moderate dimensions; such a wave guide is called an electromagnetic horn. The field components inside a sectoral horn and a conical horn have been derived in Chapter II, and to these the Smythe diffraction formula can be applied. Evaluation of the resulting integrals is, however, rather complicated. The approximate solution for the sectoral horn, given by Chu [62], is not of a form convenient for calculation.

The mouth of a sectoral horn is normally a rather narrow rectangle, and will produce a beam which is sharp in the plane of the parallel sides and comparatively broad in a plane perpendicular to them. The horn, shown in Figure 31, will be assumed to have its parallel sides

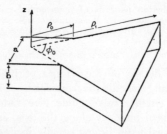

FIG. 31.—Sectoral horn fed from rectangular wave guide.

horizontal. Barrow and Chu [35, 56] have studied the variation of its beam form with flare angle and length of horn, and have obtained from the theory some general conclusions. The following facts apply to the H_{10} wave, which has its electric vector normal to the parallel sides. Considering first of all a horn of fixed length and variable flare angle, it is found that the horizontal beam angle has a minimum for a definite flare angle. This is due to the effect of two opposing factors. For small flare angles the beam is approximately that produced by a rectangular radiator of the same aperture, and thus increase of flare angle sharpens the beam. If the flare angle is large the wave inside the horn diverges considerably, and the beam angle is determined mainly by the divergence

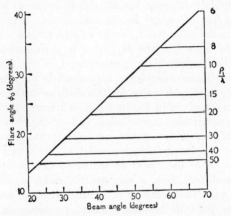

FIG. 32.—Design curve for sectoral horn (H_{10} wave), giving shortest radial length and corresponding flare angle for a specified horizontal beam. Beam angle defined by points having amplitude 10 per cent. of maximum (Chu and Barrow [56]).

of the sides ; decrease of flare angle then decreases beam angle. The sharpest beam is produced at some intermediate angle—for a horn eight wavelengths long it is about 35 degrees. The beam improves in sharpness as the length of the horn is increased, the optimum flare angle meanwhile decreasing steadily. The improvement is rapid up to a horn length of about 12 wavelengths, but thereafter is less marked. These facts are collected in the design curve of Figure 32, which provides dimensions

to give a specified beam angle. The sharpness of the
beam is always less than that which would be produced
by an H_{10} wave in a rectangular guide of the same aperture.
In practice, however, this is offset by the difficulty of
generating a pure H_{10} wave in a rectangular guide whose
dimensions are sufficiently large to allow transmission of
higher-order waves.   The presence of higher-order waves,
while it may either broaden or sharpen the primary beam,
will certainly increase the secondary lobes with a consequent loss of energy in the main beam.   The sectoral
horn, on the other hand, can be excited at such a distance
from the apex that the H_{10} wave is permitted to reach
the mouth substantially unattenuated, while high-order
waves are almost completely suppressed in the attenuation
region.   A suitable value for this distance is the value of
ρ_0 for $n = 1$ given in Figure 14, which marks the separation between the transmission and attenuation regions
for an H_{10} wave.   Excitation can be by means of a current-
carrying conductor placed parallel to the z-axis at this
distance from the apex, or the horn can be truncated
there and fed from a rectangular guide as shown in
Figure 31.   The values of ρ_0 are such that the dimension
a of the guide is between 1·2 and 1·5 times its critical
value for the H_{10} wave, and it is thus a convenient size
for a feeder.   The curves of Figures 14 and 32 are
sufficient for the complete specification of the dimensions
of a sectoral horn to produce a given beam angle in the
horizontal (ρ, ϕ) plane.   Since the vertical radiation pattern depends mainly on the separation of the parallel
sides of the horn, it is similar to that produced by a
rectangular radiator of equal vertical aperture, and has
a beam angle given approximately by (6.5).

Maximum gain does not quite coincide with minimum
beam angle, but is sufficiently close to it that, for any
length ρ_1, the angle ϕ_0 given in Figure 32 is roughly the
optimum.   The gain obtainable is somewhat less than

that which would be given by a pure H_{10} wave in a rectangular guide of the same aperture—about 80 per cent with optimum flare angle. Sets of gain curves are given in a paper by Chu and Barrow [56].

The application of the diffraction theory to conical horns is incomplete. Experimental work [55] has shown that the general properties are similar to those of the sectoral horn. For a fixed length of horn there is an optimum cone angle which gives the narrowest beam—an angle of 50 degrees for a horn three wavelengths long has been found; longer horns require smaller cone angles to give minimum beam angle; beyond a certain limit further increase of horn length gives small improvement in beam angle.

Reports of experimental work indicate that electromagnetic horns compare most favourably with other types of aerial array. Gain and beam angle are comparable with the best of similar size, and freedom from secondary lobes is notable. They require no critical adjustment, since there is no focus at which exciter elements must be placed, and no accurate phasing of several elements is necessary. Because of this property a horn radiator is capable of operating efficiently over a wide frequency range, of the order of two to one.

Dielectric rods are also used, singly or in arrays, as radiators [98, 99]. Excitation takes place at one end by connection to a wave guide or other means, and the radiation, which takes place along the length, is predominantly in the direction of the rod. Some theoretical and empirical relationships are known for the effects of diameter, dielectric constant, and length.

CHAPTER VII

RECTANGULAR GUIDE TECHNIQUES

THE rectangular guide in its H_{10} mode is the form used most frequently, and for it many associated components and techniques have been evolved. These often necessitate or deliberately introduce a discontinuity in dimensions. The mathematical difficulties associated with the treatment of such discontinuities are formidable and beyond the scope of this book, but the results are so useful that we quote them here for a number of the more fundamental techniques. There is no attempt to deal with the many uses of the diverse devices based on them: for these the reader is referred to more descriptive books [72, 73].

DIAPHRAGMS

It has been noted that a thin metallic obstacle placed across a wave guide can be regarded as a parallel impedance. Such obstacles are often used as matching impedances, the

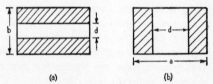

(a)   (b)

FIG. 33.—Diaphragms in rectangular wave guide:
(a) capacitive, (b) inductive.

commonest being the diaphragms shown in Figure 33 (a, b). Two different methods of approach, due to Macfarlane [104] and to Miles [103], show that the diaphragm of Figure 33 (a) is equivalent to a lumped capacitance placed across a transmission line having a normalized admittance (with respect to the wave admittance $1/Z_z$) given by

$$Y = i\frac{4b}{\lambda_t} \log_e \operatorname{cosec} \frac{\pi d}{2b}. \quad . \quad . \quad . \quad (7.1)$$

That shown in Figure 33 (b) is equivalent to a lumped inductance with a normalized admittance

$$Y = -i\frac{\lambda_t}{a} \cot^2 \frac{\pi d}{2a}. \quad . \quad . \quad . \quad (7.2)$$

A superposition of these two types can be represented as a parallel inductance and capacitance which, at resonance, will be equivalent to a high parallel resistance and so have negligible effect on the transmission of the wave.

CHANGE OF CROSS-SECTION

The same methods can be applied to discontinuities such as that shown in Figure 34, which represents a junction between two rectangular guides differing in their small

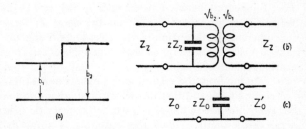

Fig. 34.—Equivalent circuits for change of cross-section in rectangular wave guide.

dimensions. These guides have the same wave impedance, but this cannot imply that they are matched since there is an abrupt change of field configuration with consequent reflexion. It can be shown [103] that the equivalent circuit is as given in Figure 34 : two transmission lines of the same characteristic impedance connected by an ideal transformer with turns ratio $\sqrt{b_2} : \sqrt{b_1}$ (an impedance ratio of $b_2 : b_1$), and a parallel capacitance. The normalized impedance Z of this capacitance is given by

$$Z = \frac{1}{2i}\left[\left(\frac{\lambda_t}{2b_1}\right)^2 - 1\right]^{\frac{1}{2}} \Big/ \log_e\left[\frac{1-\alpha^2}{4\alpha}\left(\frac{1+\alpha}{1-\alpha}\right)^{\frac{\alpha+1/\alpha}{2}}\right], \quad (7.3)$$

where $\alpha = b_1/b_2$. If the guide impedance is redefined to be proportional to b, the transformer ratio becomes unity, and the equivalent circuit of the discontinuity is reduced to a simple shunt element. This is so when the characteristic impedance of the guide defined in (4.4) is used. The normalized value of the shunt impedance is not dependent on the definition of guide impedance.

A change of cross-section in the a-dimension is more difficult to deal with, and its equivalent circuit is a four-terminal network.

T-JUNCTIONS AND SLOTS

For T-junctions between rectangular guides two main types are possible—the *series* T and the *shunt* T, these being junctions in the plane of the electric field and the magnetic field respectively, as shown in Figure 35. For the arrangement of Figure 35 (*a*) it is easy to see that a wave entering from the vertical limb suffers a discontinuity of electric field, and that the fields transmitted into the other two limbs are in antiphase, while the magnetic field has no discontinuity. Thus the scattering is anti-symmetrical, giving the junction the properties of a series circuit discussed in Chapter IV. For Figure 35 (*b*), however, it is the magnetic field which is disturbed ; the scattering is symmetrical, and the two horizontal limbs can be regarded as being in parallel with the third. Obviously the problem is more complex than these simple considerations indicate ; a more exact treatment has been given by Allanson, Cooper and Cowling [102].

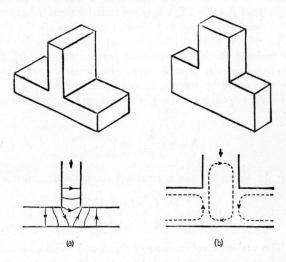

Fig. 35.—T-junctions : (a) series, (b) shunt.

A slot cut in the wall of a guide in such a way as to interrupt the flow of current will also act as a series or

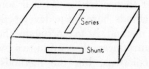

Fig. 36.—Radiating slots in rectangular wave guide.

parallel impedance. Considerations similar to those for junctions will hold for the slots shown in Figure 36.

8

Consequently the slot in the broad face is a series slot and that in the narrow face is a shunt slot. The equivalent circuit is a transmission line with a series or parallel impedance $Z = R + iX$, where the resistive term is included to account for power lost by radiation through the slot. If the slot is narrow this representation is accurate, and by making the length resonant (approximately $\lambda/2$) the reactive term can be made zero. For a narrow series slot the resistance at resonance, normalized with respect to the wave impedance of the guide, is given [109] approximately by

$$R = 0{\cdot}52\frac{\lambda_t{}^3}{ab\lambda}\cos^2\frac{\pi\lambda}{4a}. \quad . \quad . \quad . \quad (7.4)$$

For the shunt slot the normalized shunt conductance is

$$G = 0{\cdot}13\frac{\lambda^3\lambda_t}{a^3b}\left[\frac{\cos(\pi\lambda/2\lambda_t)}{1-(\lambda/\lambda_t)^2}\right]^2 . \quad . \quad . \quad (7.5)$$

The various combinations of shunt and series couplings when two guides are coupled together by a common slot in their walls have been investigated by Watson [73], [103].

CORRUGATED GUIDES

In all the wave guides so far treated the phase velocity has been greater than $c/(\varepsilon\mu)^{\frac{1}{2}}$. This is sometimes inconvenient, and methods have been developed to reduce the velocity. One method is to corrugate the walls of the guide. This introduces discontinuities which preclude any simple calculations, but the methods used can be illustrated by the example of a plane corrugated conducting sheet.

Let the sheet be as shown in Figure 37, infinite in the yz plane, with corrugations of depth l, width d, and separation D. Let a wave be propagated over its surface in the z-direction, with a phase constant β, independent of the y-coordinate. For the region $x > 0$ an E-wave

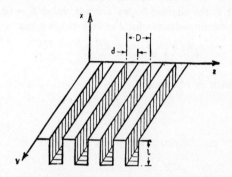

FIG. 37.—Corrugated guiding surface.

solution of the propagation equation (2.11) can be taken as

$$U = \exp[-i\beta z - \{\beta^2 - (\omega/v)^2\}^{\frac{1}{2}}x],$$

with field components given by

$$E_z = \{\beta^2 - (\omega/v)^2\}^{\frac{1}{2}}U, \quad E_x = -i\beta U, \quad H_y = -(i\omega\varepsilon/c)U.$$

Now, inside each slot a plane wave with components E_z and H_y can be propagated in the direction of $-x$ with the free wave velocity $c/(\varepsilon\mu)^{\frac{1}{2}}$, and reflected at the bottom to form a stationary wave. Thus each slot is equivalent to a length l of transmission line, short-circuited at the end. Its wave impedance being $(\mu/\varepsilon)^{\frac{1}{2}}$, the ratio of E_z to H_y at the surface is given by

$$\left[\frac{E_z}{H_y}\right]_{x=0} = i\left(\frac{\mu}{\varepsilon}\right)^{\frac{1}{2}} \tan\frac{\omega l}{v}.$$

If D is small compared with λ, then E_z can be assumed constant over the aperture of a slot and zero between slots.

The field for $x > 0$ has now to be fitted to this, which can be done by taking a Fourier sum of an infinite series of modes. A simple approximation is to represent the slot field at the surface by an average value $\bar{E}_z = (d/D)E_z$.

Equating impedances for the two fields gives

$$i\frac{d}{D}\left(\frac{\mu}{\varepsilon}\right)^{\frac{1}{2}} \tan \frac{\omega l}{v} = \frac{\{\beta^2 - (\omega/v)^2\}^{\frac{1}{2}}}{-i\omega\varepsilon/c},$$

from which is obtained

$$\beta = \frac{\omega}{v}\left[1 + \left(\frac{d}{D} \tan \frac{\omega l}{v}\right)^2\right]^{\frac{1}{2}} \quad . \quad . \quad . \quad (7.6)$$

Thus for air dielectric the phase velocity v' is

$$v' = \frac{c}{\left[1 + \left(\frac{d}{D} \tan \frac{2\pi l}{\lambda}\right)^2\right]^{\frac{1}{2}}}, \quad . \quad . \quad (7.7)$$

so that $v' < c$. For the range of slot depth $0 < l < \lambda/4$ the amplitude decreases exponentially above the surface, and so the energy travels predominantly close to the surface. Thus for a slot depth less than $\lambda/4$ the surface acts as a guiding surface for the wave. For depths where $\lambda/4 < l < \lambda/2$ the sign of the exponential index is changed and the wave diverges from the surface.

Similar treatments show that, for corrugated rectangular and circular guides, the phase velocity can be reduced to any required value by a suitable adjustment of dimensions [118], [72]. This reduction of phase velocity to a value less than the velocity of light is particularly important in applications where a beam of electrons is required to move at approximately the phase velocity of the wave, as in the linear accelerator or the travelling wave amplifier.

Another method of obtaining the same result is by lining the walls of the guide with dielectric material. In this case an exact solution of the equations is readily obtainable [112], [115], [116]. A flat surface covered with a layer of dielectric material has properties similar to the corrugated surface, and acts also as a guiding surface [113].

These are all examples of an increasingly important technique of loading wave guides to give them the properties required for particular applications. Periodic loading, as in the corrugated forms, produces a structure which acts like a band-pass filter having an infinite number of pass bands. The form of the relation between phase velocity and frequency is often a major consideration in design.

BIBLIOGRAPHY

WAVE GUIDE TRANSMISSION LINES

General

1. O. Lodge, *Proc. Roy. Instn*, **14**, 321 (1894).
2. Lord Rayleigh, *Phil. Mag.*, **43**, 125 (1897).
3. T. J. I'a. Bromwich, *Phil. Mag.*, **38**, 143 (1919).
4. L. Brillouin, *Rev. Gén. Élect.*, **40**, 227 (1936).
5. S. A. Schelkunoff, *Proc. Inst. Radio Engrs*, **25**, 1457 (1937).
6. L. Page and N. I. Adams, Jr., *Phys. Rev.*, **52**, 647 (1937).
7. L. Brillouin, *Elect. Commun.*, **16**, 350 (1938); *Bull. Soc. Franç. Élect.*, **8**, 899 (1938).
8. H. Buchholz, *Elekt. NachrTech.*, **15**, 297 (1938).
9. H. W. Droste, *Telegr.-u. FernsprTech.*, **27**, 199, **273**, **310**, 337 (1938).
10. S. M. Rytov, *J. Phys., Moscow*, **2**, 187 (1940).
11. H. R. L. Lamont, *Phil. Mag.*, **29**, 521, **30**, 1 (1940).
12. M. Ito, *Electrotech. J., Tokyo*, **4**, 247 (1940).
13. J. E. Houldin, *G.E.C. Jl*, **11**, 172 (1941).
14. W. L. Barrow and H. Schaevitz, *Elect. Engng, N.Y.*, **60**, 119 (1941).

Rectangular Guides

15. L. J. Chu and W. L. Barrow, *Proc. Inst. Radio Engrs*, **26**, 1520 (1938).
16. H. Riedel, *Hochfrequenztech. u. Elektroakust.*, **53**, 122 (1939).
17. J. Kemp, *J. Instn Elect. Engrs*, **88**, III, 213 (1941).

Circular Guides

18. W. L. Barrow, *Proc. Inst. Radio Engrs*, **24**, 1298 (1936).
19. G. C. Southworth, *Bell Syst. Tech. J.*, **15**, 284 (1936).
20. J. R. Carson, S. P. Mead, and S. A. Schelkunoff, *Bell. Syst. Tech. J.*, **15**, 310 (1936).
21. G. C. Southworth, *Proc. Inst. Radio Engrs*, **25**, 807 (1937).
22. S. Sonoda, *Electrotech. J., Tokyo*, **1**, 214 (1937).

23. A. G. Clavier, *Bull. Soc. Franç. Élect.*, **8**, 355 (1938) ; *Elect. Commun.*, **17**, 276 (1939).

24. A. G. Clavier and V. Altovsky, *Bull. Soc. Franç. Élect.*, **8**, 793 (1938).

25. A. G. Clavier and V. Altovsky, *Rev. Gén. Élect.*, **45**, 697, 731 (1939) ; *Elect. Commun.*, **18**, 81 (1939).

26. J. R. Carson, *J. Amer. Inst. Elect. Engrs*, **43**, 908 (1924).

27. S. A. Schelkunoff, *Bell Syst. Tech. J.*, **13**, 532 (1934).

Dielectric Guides

28. D. Hondros and P. Debye, *Ann. Phys., Lpz.*, **32**, 465 (1910).

29. H. Zahn, *Ann. Phys., Lpz.*, **49**, 907 (1916).

30. O. Schriever, *Ann. Phys., Lpz.*, **63**, 645 (1920).

31. E. Kašpar, *Ann. Phys., Lpz.*, **32**, 353 (1938).
    Also 9, **20**.

Elliptic Guides

32. S. A. Schelkunoff, *J. Appl. Phys.*, **9**, 484 (1938).

33. L. J. Chu, *J. Appl. Phys.*, **9**, 583 (1938).

34. A. W. Melloh, *Proc. Inst. Radio Engrs*, **28**, 179 (1940).
    Also 7.

Flared and Curved Guides

35. W. L. Barrow and L. J. Chu, *Proc. Inst. Radio Engrs*, **27**, 51 (1939).

36. H. Buchholz, *Ann. Phys., Lpz.*, **37**, 173 (1940).

37. S. Sonoda, S. Morimoto, *Electrotech. J., Tokyo*, **4**, 41, 64 (1940).

38. H. Buchholz, *Elekt. Nachr.-Tech.*, **16**, 73 (1939).

RESONATORS

39. A. Kalähne, *Ann. Phys., Lpz.*, **18**, 92 (1905) ; **19**, 80, 879 (1906).

40. J. W. Nicholson, *Phil. Mag.*, **11**, 703 (1906).

41. W. W. Hansen, *J. Appl. Phys.*, **9**, 654 (1938).

42. W. W. Hansen and R. D. Richtmyer, *J. Appl. Phys.*, **10**, 189 (1939).

43. R. D. Richtmyer, *J. Appl. Phys.*, **10**, 391 (1939).

44. F. Borgnis, *Ann. Phys., Lpz.*, **35**, 359 (1939).

45. M. Jouguet, *C.R. Acad. Sci., Paris*, **209**, 25, 203 (1939).

46. F. Borgnis, *Hochfrequenztech. u. Elektroakust.*, **54**, 121 (1939).

47. J. Müller, *Hochfrequenztech. u. Elektroakust.*, **54**, 157 (1939).

48. H. Buchholz, *Hochfrequenztech. u. Elektroakust.*, **54**, 161 (1939).

49. W. L. Barrow and W. W. Mieher, *Proc. Inst. Radio Engrs*, **28**, 184 (1940).
50. M. Watanabe, *Electrotech. J.*, *Tokyo*, **5**, 7 (1941).
51. E. U. Condon, *J. Appl. Phys.*, **12**, 129 (1941).

RADIATORS

52. L. Bergmann and L. Krügel, *Ann. Phys.*, *Lpz.*, **21**, 113 (1934).
53. W. L. Barrow and F. M. Greene, *Proc. Inst. Radio Engrs*, **26**, 1498 (1938).
54. W. L. Barrow and F. D. Lewis, *Proc. Inst. Radio Engrs*, **27**, 41 (1939).
55. G. C. Southworth and A. P. King, *Proc. Inst. Radio Engrs*, **27**, 95 (1939).
56. L. J. Chu and W. L. Barrow, *Elect. Engng*, *N.Y.*, **58**, 333 (1939).
57. S. A. Schelkunoff, *Phys. Rev.*, **56**, 308 (1939).
58. J. A. Stratton and L. J. Chu, *Phys. Rev.*, **56**, 99 (1939).
59. W. L. Barrow, L. J. Chu, and J. J. Jansen, *Proc. Inst. Radio Engrs*, **27**, 769 (1939).
60. S. Sonoda, *Electrotech. J.*, *Tokyo*, **4**, 35, 142 (1940).
61. W. L. Barrow and C. Shulman, *Proc. Inst. Radio Engrs*, **28**, 130 (1940).
62. L. J. Chu, *J. Appl. Phys.*, **11**, 603 (1940).
    Also (35).

GENERAL REFERENCES

63. J. McMahon, *Math. Ann.*, **9**, 23 (1895).
64. F. Kottler, *Ann. Phys.*, *Lpz.*, **71**, 457 (1923).
65. S. A. Schelkunoff, *Bell Syst. Tech. J.*, **17**, 17 (1938).

ADDITIONAL BIBLIOGRAPHY

WAVE GUIDE TRANSMISSION LINES

General

66. R. D. Spence and C. P. Wells, *Phys. Rev.*, **62**, 58 (1942) (Parabolic guide).
67. S. A. Schelkunoff, *Quart. Appl. Math.*, **2**, 1 (1944).
68. W. D. Hershberger, *J. Appl. Phys.*, **16**, 465 (1945).
69. J. C. Slater, *Rev. Mod. Phys.*, **18**, 441 (1946).
70. S. B. Cohn, *Proc. Inst. Radio Engrs*, **35**, 783 (1947) (Ridged guide).
71. J. Oswald, *Câbles et Transm.*, **1**, 205 (1947).
72. L. G. H. Huxley, *A Survey of the Principles and Practice of Wave Guides*, Cambridge University Press, 1947.
73. W. H. Watson, *The Physical Principles of Wave Guide Transmission and Antenna Systems*, Oxford University Press, 1947.

Rectangular Guides

74. A. Käch, *Helv. Phys. Acta*, **20**, 341 (1947).
75. A. C. Bartlett, *Wireless Engr*, **25**, 202 (1948).

Circular Guides

76. H. Bondi and S. Kuhn, *Wireless Engr*, **24**, 222 (1947).

Curved Guides

77. K. Riess, *Quart. Appl. Math.*, **1**, 328 (1944).
78. W. J. Albersheim, *Bell Syst. Tech. J.*, **28**, 1 (1949).
79. M. Jouguet, *Câbles et Transm.*, **1**, 39, 133 (1947); **2**, 257 (1948).
80. S. O. Rice, *Bell Syst. Tech. J.*, **27**, 305 (1948).

RESONATORS

81. W. C. Hahn, *J. Appl. Phys.*, **12**, 62 (1941).
82. K. F. Niessen, *Physica*, **8**, 1077 (1941); **9**, 145 (1942).
83. F. Borgnis, *Hochfrequenztech. u. Elektroakust.*, **59**, 22 (1942); **60**, 151 (1942).

84. M. Jouguet, *Rev. Gén. Élect.*, **51**, 318, 484 (1942).
85. E. Lednigg, *Ann. Phys., Lpz*, **41**, 537 (1942).
86. D. Middleton, *Phys. Rev.*, **63**, 343 (1943).
87. E. Lednigg, *Hochfrequenztech. u. Elektroakust.*, **62**, 38 (1943).
88. J. R. Whinnery, C. Concordia, W. Ridgway, and G. Kron, *Proc. Inst. Radio Engrs*, **32**, 360 (1944).
89. F. Horner, T. A. Taylor, R. Dunsmuir, J. Lamb, and W. Jackson, *J. Instn. Elect. Engrs*, Pt. III, **93**, 53 (1946).
90. I. G. Wilson, C. W. Schramm, and J. P. Kinzer, *Bell Syst. Tech. J.*, **25**, 408 (1946).
91. S. Roberts and A. von Hippel, *J. Appl. Phys.*, **17**, 610 (1946).
92. J. Bernier, *Onde Élect.*, **26**, 305 (1946).
93. H. Motz, *J. Instn. Elect. Engrs*, Pt. IIIA, **93**, 335 (1946).
94. J. P. Kinzer and I. G. Wilson, *Bell Syst. Tech. J.*, **26**, 31, 410 (1947). (Good bibliography in latter.)
95. K. F. Niessen, *Appl. Sci. Res.*, B1, 18, 187 (1947–8).
96. R. N. Bracewell, *Proc. Inst. Radio Engrs*, **35**, 830 (1947). Also 101.

RADIATORS

97. H. A. Bethe, *Phys. Rev.*, **66**, 163 (1944).
98. D. F. Halliday and D. G. Kiely, *J. Instn. Elect. Engrs*, Pt. IIIA, **94**, 610 (1947).
99. G. E. Mueller and W. A. Tyrrell, *Bell Syst. Tech. J.*, **26**, 837 (1947).
100. W. R. Smythe, *Phys. Rev.*, **72**, 1066 (1947).
101. W. R. Smythe, *Rev. Mod. Phys.*, **20**, 175 (1948).

TECHNIQUES

Diaphragms, Slots, Junctions, &c.

102. J. T. Allanson, R. Cooper, and T. G. Cowling, *J. Instn. Elect. Engrs*, Pt. IIIA, **93**, 117 (1946).
103. J. W. Miles, *Proc. Inst. Radio Engrs*, **34**, 728 (1946).
104. G. G. Macfarlane, *J. Instn. Elect. Engrs*, Pt. IIIA, **93**, 703 (1946).
105. M. Surdin, *J. Instn. Elect. Engrs*, Pt. IIIA, **93**, 725 (1946).
106. W. H. Watson, *J. Instn. Elect. Engrs*, Pt. IIIA, **93**, 747 (1946).
107. N. Elson, *Wireless Engr*, **24**, 44 (1947).
108. W. A. Tyrrell, *Proc. Inst. Radio Engrs*, **35**, 1295 (1947).
109. A. F. Stevenson, *J. Appl. Phys.*, **19**, 24 (1948).
110. H. A. Wheeler, *Proc. Inst. Radio Engrs*, **36**, 478 (1948).
111. G. Saxon and C. W. Miller, *Wireless Engr*, **25**, 138 (1948).

Loaded Wave Guides

112. L. Pincherle, *Phys. Rev.*, **66**, 118 (1944).
113. D. W. Fry, *J. Instn. Elect. Engrs*, Pt. IIIA, **93**, 1497 (1946'
114. A. M. Woodward, *Wireless Engr*, **24**, 192 (1947).
115. S. Frankel, *J. Appl. Phys.*, **18**, 650 (1947).
116. G. G. Bruck and E. R. Wicher, *J. Appl. Phys.*, **18**, 776 (1947); *Onde Élect.*, **27**, 470 (1947).
117. E. L. Chu and W. W. Hansen, *J. Appl. Phys.*, **18**, 996 (1947).
118. L. Brillouin, *J. Appl. Phys.*, **19**, 1023 (1948) (see also **20**, 634 (1949).
119. W. Walkinshaw, *Proc. Phys. Soc.*, **61**, 246 (1948).

GENERAL REFERENCES

120. N. W. McLachlan, *Theory and Application of Mathieu Functions*, Oxford University Press, 1947.
121. H. B. Dwight, *J. Math. Phys.*, **27**, 84 (1948).
122. M. Kline, *J. Math. Phys.*, **27**, 37 (1948).

INDEX